Omega-Z Diet for Weight Loss: Workbook

Originally published in paperback by Amazon.

Paperback: ISBN 978-1-7360024-2-1

Front Cover Credit: Tharin White

Graphic Image Credit: Kayla Follin and Tharin White

Formatting Credit: Kayla Follin

Acknowledgments

Special thanks and recognition go to the following exceptional people for their support, work, and ideas for this project.

To my mother, Linda Donohoe, for her constant encouragement and support.

To my friend and colleague, Lynzi Glasscock, M.P.H., whose organizational, fact checking, and creativity skills were heavily relied upon throughout the creation and execution of this project.

To Caesar Toland for his creative and nutritious recipes.

To Renata Yassa, Presley Riden, and John Kebles for their flexibility and willingness to flip-flop roles as needs emerged.

To Tharin White and Kayla Follin for their ideas, creativity, and skills used in developing many appealing images and icons that increase the user-friendliness of this book. And a special thanks to Kayla Follin who received and adjusted all kinds of documents, images, and ideas and pulled them all together to make a beautifully formatted book.

Contents

Introducing the Omega-Z Diet

Let me shock you: losing weight is not difficult! Most people on a diet will lose weight, sometimes lots of weight! Even on fad diets! So why do so many people have unwanted, excess body fat? The problem isn't the inability to lose weight; the problems are making sure the weight lost is fat weight and making sure that fat is both lost safely and kept off permanently.

The Academy of Nutrition and Dietetics takes the position that successful treatment of excess weight and obesity requires adopting and maintaining healthy behaviors that influence food consumption and promote physical activity for life. Various health behaviors have been studied for a long time, and results suggest that behaviors are influenced by many things. Thus, to increase the chances of success with weight loss and weight maintenance, it is wise for several interventions to be incorporated at various levels. In the pages that follow, many techniques, suggestions, and recommendations will be shared, which will ultimately lead to success.

The reason the Omega-Z Diet is so remarkably helpful is that it brings together the best elements and features from all the best-rated diets to make one foolproof, soundly researched, flexible diet that is easily understood. Talk about pulling good stuff together and putting it in one place! The guidelines are easy to follow. What are we waiting for? Let's get started!

Questions to Ask Your Doctor

When starting any new diet, it is always a good idea to consult a physician and ask:

- Is this diet plan a reasonable approach for me to lose weight?
- How much weight do I need to lose?
- Should I make any adjustments to following the plan?
- Should I take any vitamins or other supplements while on this plan?
- Is the exercise required by the plan suitable for me?
- Is this diet a healthy option for me?

Omega-Z Diet Guidelines

The Omega-Z Guidelines address the following important areas:

Variety

The Omega-Z Diet Plan recommends choosing a variety of foods. This means consuming foods from all the food groups daily. It also means making sure to choose different foods from within the same group. Meals should be colorful. Doing this will ensure a variety of nutrients are consumed, reduce boredom, introduce different flavors and aromas, and make meals more attractive with the added colors and textures.

- Choose different foods from within each food group. For example, do not eat a banana every morning. Instead, have a banana one morning, blueberries the next, a peach the next, and so on. Do not eat carrots every day; instead, mix and combine different vegetables daily.

- Work your way around the food rainbow, choosing different colors.

Balance

The Omega-Z Diet Plan ensures a balanced diet. It is designed to provide adequate protein, fat, carbohydrates, water, vitamins, and minerals at each calorie level. Meals are designed to provide satiety, volume, and flavor. To maximize the benefits of balance:

- Consume meals and snacks throughout the day.

- Stay well hydrated.

- If on a lower calorie level (1400-1600), consider taking a multi-vitamin.

- Weigh and measure foods to start until your eye is trained to identify the amount of food equaling a serving size.

Fiber

The Omega-Z Diet Plan provides adequate fiber. To maximize fiber:

- Regularly select whole-grain options for starches.

- When shopping for bread and cereal, make sure the words "Whole grain" are the first ingredient.

- When baking, substitute half whole-grain flour for white flour.

- Eat the peels and skins of apples, pears, grapes, peaches, and baked potatoes.

- Eat berries.

- Lentils are a great source of protein and fiber.

- Choose nuts to fulfill your need for dietary fat.

- Add seeds to cereals and casseroles.

Micronutrients

The Omega-Z Diet Plan is balanced, full of variety, and eliminates no food groups. It emphasizes whole foods and can provide adequate vitamins and minerals. Tips to help inspire and increase the incorporation of whole fruits and vegetables include:

- Vary between raw and cooked vegetables.
- Experiment with different herbs and spices on vegetables to make them more interesting.
- Add different fruits to yogurt and cereal.
- Plan meals around vegetables. In other words, think about the vegetables in a dish first.
- Snack on fruits and vegetables.
- Add vegetables to soups, casseroles, and sandwiches.
- Keep fresh fruits and vegetables in sight, easily accessible and ready to eat.
- Add a greater amount of vegetables to dishes than the recipe states.

Carbohydrates

The Omega-Z Diet Plan emphasizes complex carbohydrates and provides adequate amounts of carbohydrates for fuel, health, and proper function. The Omega-Z Diet Plan supplies 45–65% of all its calories from carbohydrates, which falls within the AMDR recommendations. To maximize the benefits of carbohydrates:

- Choose whole-grain cereals, crackers, and grains.
- If you are not accustomed to the flavor or texture of whole grains, start slowly but persist.
- Breakfast is a simple way to incorporate whole grains, and it helps spread out calories throughout the day.

Protein

The Omega-Z Diet Plan provides adequate protein for growth and repair of lean tissue and for overall health. The AMDR for protein is 10–35% of all calories. Each calorie level in the Omega-Z Diet Plan provides approximately 22% of its calories from protein, well within the recommended range.

- Choose healthy proteins, such as lean meat, fish, and plant-based proteins like beans and legumes. (Select foods that have the "chicken leg" icon instead of the "steak" or "bacon" icons.)
- If you prefer plant-based protein, be sure to consume a variety of foods to ensure all essential amino acids are provided.

Fat

The Omega-Z Diet provides the appropriate amount of fat according to the AMDR recommendation of 20–35%. Use the following suggestions when making fat selections.

- Choose meat with the least amount of visible fat.
- Trim visible fat from meat and remove skin from poultry before cooking.
- Choose mostly monounsaturated and polyunsaturated fats.

- Minimize unhealthy fats, such as trans-fats and saturated fats.

- A good non-stick pan can help you cook without butter or oil.

- Choose reduced-calorie or fat-free dressings.

Moderation

The Omega-Z Diet includes appropriate serving sizes for each calorie level and allows for occasional dessert, junk food, or eating out. It does not take an all-or-nothing approach. It avoids excess and extremes, is based on accepted guidelines, and stays within reasonable limits.

- Cook and pre-package meals in advance.

- After eating a meal, if you want to eat more, leave the table and do something active or simply wait 20 minutes to see if you still want to eat more. If the answer is yes, choose more vegetables or fruit.

- Whenever possible, eat real food instead of boxed convenience foods that have been highly processed. These serving sizes tend to be smaller and less filling.

- Try to avoid eating out unless you preplan it and it fits into your meal plan. Portion sizes at restaurants and fast-food establishments are usually not presented in moderation, and food items are filled with empty calories.

- Enjoy foods at celebrations and gatherings, just be sure to take small portions.

Individual Differences

The Omega-Z Diet is geared towards healthy individuals who want to lose weight. As such, it can be tailored to each person's needs, as it considers lifestyle factors. It is flexible, so as to work with different schedules, tastes, food availability, budgets, and of course, calorie requirements. It allows individuals the flexibility to eat with their families and friends.

- Determine the number of calories you need daily to lose weight safely.

- Once you have selected the calorie level, personalize your food selections and distribute them throughout the day in a way that works for you. Ideally, 3 meals and 2–3 snacks should be consumed daily. Consumption of food should be spread throughout the day. Try to eat something every 3–4 hours to avoid severe hunger.

- Set personal, realistic daily goals. For example: "Today, I will walk 8,000 steps."

- Set personal, realistic weekly goals. For example: "This week, I will complete my exercise routine 3 times."

- Set personal, realistic monthly goals. For example: "By the end of the month, I will lose 5 pounds." Or "By the end of the month, I will lose 6–7 pounds."

Exercise Is Recommended

Exercise is an important component of weight management and weight loss. There are several reasons exercise is important. As we age, we lose muscle mass. The only way to keep muscle mass as the years pass is to work it. This means exercise. Exercise preserves muscle mass during weight loss, maintains basal metabolic rate, and promotes weight loss through increased energy expenditure. Because people attempting to lose weight are vulnerable to losing lean tissue during the weight-loss process, exercise becomes especially important for anyone trying to lose body fat. One pound of excess body fat stores about 3,500 calories of energy.

- Aim to participate in moderate-intensity physical activity 3 to 5 days each week, for a total of 150 minutes weekly.

- Supplement with lifting weights, flexibility, and balance training.
- Track and record your activity. Monitoring progress keeps us honest and can be very inspiring and motivating.
- Aim to burn 300 to 400 calories per workout session.
- Don't aim to lose more than 2 pounds per week.
- Set realistic timelines and realistic goals.
- Determine how many calories you need to achieve the goals you have set.
- Depending on your starting physical condition, aim for 65–75% of heart rate max (HRmax) for 30–45 minutes.

The Omega-Z Diet does not dictate the type of exercise in which you should engage. You might ask yourself, "What is the best type of exercise?" Some say swimming is, because it involves the whole body, is low impact, and includes both cardio and resistance. But if you don't know how to swim or don't have easy access to a pool.... guess what? Swimming is not the best exercise. The best exercise is the exercise you will do on a regular basis. It could be fun, it could be social, or it could be private alone time. You pick, you are in control. Make it work for you.

Target Exercise Heart Rates

The table below displays heart rate ranges for different ages. Maximum heart rate is often determined by the formula 220 minus your age. In the table below, find the age category closest to yours.

Age	Target HR Zone 50–85%	Average Maximum Heart Rate,100%
20 years	100–170 bpm*	200 bpm*
30 years	95–162 bpm*	190 bpm*
35 years	93–157 bpm*	185 bpm*
40 years	90–153 bpm*	180 bpm*
45 years	88–149 bpm*	175 bpm*
50 years	85–145 bpm*	170 bpm*
55 years	83–140 bpm*	165 bpm*
60 years	80–136 bpm*	160 bpm*
65 years	78–132 bpm*	155 bpm*
70 years	75–128 bpm*	150 bpm*

Adapted from the American Heart Association: www.heart.org/en/healthy-living/fitness/fitness-basics/target-heart-rates
*bpm = beats per minute
These figures are approximations to be used as a general guide.

- For those desiring to exercise at "Moderate Intensity," your target heart rate during physical activities should be about 50–70% of maximum heart rate.
- For those who can exercise more vigorously, "Vigorous Intensity" is about 70–85% of maximum heart rate.

Keep in mind, everyone starts at different levels of fitness. Exercise intensity can also be reflected in our perceived exertion, breathing, sweat rate, and how tired our muscles feel. If you are not fit or are just beginning an exercise program, aim for the lower end of your target heart rate, and always talk to a doctor if you have any medical conditions or are not sure how intensely to exercise.

Enjoyment of Food

The Omega-Z Diet Plan features a mindfulness approach to eating, allows eating to be social/something the whole family can enjoy, and recommends foods that are tasty and appealing.

- Make mealtimes enjoyable.
- Play restaurant music in the background.
- Set out a tablecloth, fine china, and maybe a candle; make the meal a big deal.
- Garnish meals like restaurants do.
- Use fresh, appetizing foods.
- Use spices liberally for your personal taste.
- Plan to include treats in small portions.
- Slow down and enjoy the conversation of those around you.
- Focus on your food. Do not engage in other activities like watching television or working on a computer while eating.
- Don't eat food out of a container; a plate helps you appreciate what you are eating more.
- Have a family competition to see who can make the evening meal the most pleasurable experience. Be creative and have fun.
- Make the experience a memorable one worthy of those calories.

Easy to Understand

The Omega-Z Diet Plan provides a user-friendly system and is backed by scientific principles.

- Familiarize yourself with items and portion sizes on the Omega-Z Food List.
- Train your eye to identify the appropriate portion sizes of various foods.
- Choose from a wide variety of whole foods.

Sustainability

The Omega-Z Diet Plan includes sustainable maintenance and transition ideas, as it builds skills that are helpful for maintaining weight loss long-term. It is not strict, unhealthy, monotonous, or too low in calories. Some people like the freedom to choose their own foods and meals. Others like to be told exactly what they should eat when they are trying to lose weight. The Omega-Z Diet Plan is a plan for life. That is why there is room for holidays, room to "do life" and room for celebrations and eating out. We live in an impatient society that is not accustomed to waiting. The speed of today's technology has only made us more impatient. But short-term fad diets fail. If you have tried them in the past, you know this: you've been "On" them and then go "Off" them. This approach does not work. Steady consistency brings victory.

- Avoid monotonous eating.
- Realize you cannot go back to old habits. In other words, you're never "off a balanced eating plan."
- Embrace this new lifestyle and the benefits that come with it.

- Continually set new weight goals and continually follow the Omega-Z Diet Plan.

- Continue to limit, reduce, or eliminate beverages with empty calories.

- Pay attention to portion sizes, body weight or how clothes fit, and appropriate and beneficial levels of exercise in order to maintain progress.

Long-Term Weight Loss

The Omega-Z Diet Plan promotes many healthy skills and slow, steady weight loss, which helps keep weight off over time.

- Make it your goal to lose between ½ and 2 pounds a week.

- Do not engage in fasts or cleanses that can promote the development of an unhealthy relationship with food.

- Make small, slow, steady, gradual changes that equate to lifestyle changes.

- Engage in intentional eating, not mindless eating.

- Eat real, whole foods that are commonly found in most grocery stores.

- When you reach your desired weight, continue to exercise. Experiment with increasing your exercise. Try resistance training, such as lifting weights, to help prevent the loss of muscle and preserve and improve your metabolic rate.

- When you reach your desired weight, continue to eat breakfast and monitor your food intake.

- Continue to track your progress.

- Following the Omega-Z Diet Plan over time means you made sustainable lifestyle changes, rather than following hardcore, unrealistic rules; so, continue to be consistent.

- When you reach your goal weight, monitor the scale or the way your clothes fit as you add extra food in order to maintain your desired weight.

- Be aware of your stress level. Stress affects hormone levels, which negatively affect weight loss. Consider combating stress with increased exercise or yoga.

- Once you reach your goal weight, if you find yourself hungry, increase your vegetable consumption. Vegetables are nutrient-dense; they take up space in the stomach but provide few calories.

- Remember that most vegetables can be eaten liberally as long as they are not prepared with extra fats, oils, cheeses, or sauces. Consider vegetables a free food.

- Review the Basal Metabolic Rate (BMR) formula often as your weight and age numbers change. When you reach your goal weight you no longer need to subtract 500 or 1,000 calories like you did when trying to lose weight. The following guidelines show you how to gradually increase your food intake to help maintain your desired weight. The numbers in the chart represent recommended servings per day of each food group.

Food Group	2,100 Calories	2,200 Calories	2,300 Calories	2,400 Calories	2,500 Calories
Low-fat dairy	3	3	3	3	3
Low to medium fat protein	7.5	8	8.5	9	9
Starches	10	11	12	12	12.5
Fruit	4	4	5	5	5
Non-starchy vegetables	5	5	5	5	5
Fat	4	4	4	4	5

- Drink water to stay hydrated. This habit may help reduce calorie intake.
- Surround yourself with a support system of people who will be helpful, positive, and hold you accountable.
- Mentally prepare knowing there will be hard days, or weeks, so be gentle and forgiving with yourself; you are not a robot. Remember, this is a marathon, not a sprint.

Proper Education

The Omega-Z Diet Plan provides information that is accurate and based on scientific knowledge. It empowers dieters to make healthy choices. It answers the questions:

- Why do we eat what we eat?
- Why are certain food-preparation methods best?
- What nutrients are provided by various foods?
- How does the body process food?

Cost

The Omega-Z Diet Plan cost is close to the average or even below-average grocery bill.

- Eat real food and minimize eating out, which requires paying for someone else to prepare and serve your food.
- Do not buy expensive supplements.
- No need to buy organic.
- Do not pay a diet membership fee (put that money toward buying healthy foods or a gym membership!).
- Keep a coupon file and shop with it.
- Incorporate sale and seasonal items.

Calories

The Omega-Z Diet considers individual calorie differences and involves specific calorie calculations to meet individual needs. Next are 5 steps to help you determine your calorie needs.

How to Determine Caloric Intake for Weight Loss

Step 1 - Determine How Many Calories Are Needed

There are many formulas to determine calorie needs. How many calories a person needs depends on these factors:

- Height
- Weight
- Sex
- Age
- Exercise (Activity level)

These five factors should be considered when determining calorie needs, because each of these influences the number of calories burned. Any formula that ignores one of these components will not be able to accurately individualize calorie needs.

First we need to find out how many calories you need at rest. This is your Basal Metabolic Rate. Below, two formulas are provided for men and two for women. If you prefer to work with kg and cm, choose the Metric Formula. If you prefer to work in pounds and inches, choose the Imperial Formula.

To determine the number of calories needed at rest, your Basal Metabolic Rate, choose one of the formulas below:

Men	Metric	BMR = 66.5 + (13.75 x weight in kg) + (5 x height in cm) – (6.75 x age in years)
Men	Imperial	BMR = 66 + (6.2 x weight in pounds) + (12.7 x height in inches) – (6.8 x age in years)
Women	Metric	BMR = 655 + (9.6 x weight in kg) + (1.85 x height in cm) – (4.7 x age in years)
Women	Imperial	BMR = 655 + (4.4 x weight in pounds) + (4.7 x height in inches) – (4.7 x age in years)

Example: Sally

An example for a 5' 10" woman weighing 180 pounds (let's call her Sally) is provided below using first the imperial formula, then the metric formula.

Woman – Sally

45 years old

5' 10" = 70 inches

180 pounds

(Exercise will be assessed later using an activity factor.)

Imperial Formula

BMR = 655 + (4.4 x weight in pounds) + (4.7 x height in inches) - (4.7 x age in years)

BMR = 655 + (4.4 x 180 pounds) + (4.7 x 70 inches) - (4.7 x 45 years)

BMR = 655 + (792) + (329) - (212)

Sally's Answer to Step 1 (Using the Imperial Formula) = 1,564 calories

Metric Formula

BMR = 655 + (9.6 x weight in kg) + (1.85 x height in cm) – (4.7 x age in years)

BMR = 655 + (9.6 x 81.8 kg) + (1.85 x 178 cm) - (4.7 x 45)

BMR = 655 + (785) + (329) - (212)

Sally's Answer to Step 1 (Using the Metric Formula) = 1,557 calories

You will notice that the answers using the different formulas are close but do not match exactly. Looking at this, we can see that there is quite a bit of "math rounding" that takes place. The difference between the two numbers is 7 calories—a very small difference that will have no impact in the grand scheme of living life.

Men	Metric	BMR = 66.5 + (13.75 x weight in kg) + (5 x height in cm) – (6.75 x age in years)
Men	Imperial	BMR = 66 + (6.2 x weight in pounds) + (12.7 x height in inches) – (6.8 x age in years)
Women	Metric	BMR = 655 + (9.6 x weight in kg) + (1.85 x height in cm) – (4.7 x age in years)
Women	Imperial	BMR = 655 + (4.4 x weight in pounds) + (4.7 x height in inches) - (4.7 x age in years)

Your Turn: Individualize it with your numbers

Be sure to choose the correct formula (male or female), because everything we do from this point on will be based on the number you get from this equation. In the space below, copy the formula you are most comfortable using (pounds/inches or kg/cm). Then, just like the above example shows, fill in the blanks. Remember, do the math inside the parentheses ( ) first. This formula will show you your basal metabolic rate (BMR). This is the number of calories you need at rest, just because you are a living, breathing being. Circle your answer.

Step 2 – Determine Activity Factor

We cannot stop here. BMR only determines how many calories are needed at rest. You are not at rest. You are working, caring for children, walking around, and maybe exercising regularly. So now you have to multiply your BMR by an Activity Factor. This is not an exact science, so use your best judgment. As life happens, your activity level may vary. From the chart below, determine your activity factor.

Activity Factors

Little to no exercise	-	Daily calories needed	=	BMR	x	1.2
Light exercise (1–3 days per week)	-	Daily calories needed	=	BMR	x	1.375
Moderate exercise (3–5 days per week)	-	Daily calories needed	=	BMR	x	1.55
Heavy exercise (6–7 days per week)	-	Daily calories needed	=	BMR	x	1.725
Very heavy exercise (2X/ day, extra-heavy workouts)	-	Daily calories needed	=	BMR	x	1.9

Example: Sally

Sally walks for an hour twice a week with her friend. She does light housework in the evenings and has a job that keeps her sitting at her desk most days. She does not have a regular exercise routine; therefore, according to the chart above, she is classified in the "Light exercise" category, which means we will use the number 1.375 as her activity factor.

Sally's BMR is 1,564

1,564 x 1.375 = 2,150 calories

Sally's Answer to Step 2 = 2,150 calories

This tells us how many calories Sally needs daily to maintain her 180 pounds. Look over the activity factor chart above. Determine where you think you fall. This is not an exact science. It is okay if you are off to begin with. In fact, you might feel like you fall between two categories. If that is the case, choose a number between those two categories. For example, if you don't feel like you exactly fit into the moderate-exercise category (1.55), but you also don't feel like you quite fit into the heavy exercise (1.725) category either, choose a number between the two categories. Try 1.6 or 1.65. As time goes on, you will be able to tell how this number is working for you.

Your Turn: Individualize it with your numbers

In the space below, determine how many calories you need to maintain your current weight with your current physical activity by multiplying the number you got from Step 1 by your chosen Activity Factor. Circle your answer.

_________________ X _________________ = _________________________

(My BMR from Step 1) (Activity Factor) (Calories needed to maintain weight)

Step 3 – Determine Calorie Deductions for Weight Loss

Now we know how many calories are needed to maintain our current weight. This is interesting information, but in order to lose weight, we need to adjust the final answer we got in Step 2. Because this part gets even more individualized, more examples are provided. Let's meet Sally's sister Sue, who has different needs than Sally. Taking the time to review both sisters' information will allow you to see what you have in common, ultimately giving you direction for your weight loss.

Example: Sally

Sally needs 2,150 calories a day to maintain her 180 pounds. But since she wants to lose weight, we need to adjust her number to allow for weight loss. The recommended weight loss is ½-2 pounds per week. For Sally, we are going to aim for a 1-pound loss per week. This mean a 500-calorie deduction a day. (500 calories x 7 days = 3,500 calories) 3,500 calories = 1 pound.

Men	Metric	BMR = 66.5 + (13.75 x weight in kg) + (5 x height in cm) – (6.75 x age in years)
Men	Imperial	BMR = 66 + (6.2 x weight in pounds) + (12.7 x height in inches) – (6.8 x age in years)
Women	Metric	BMR = 655 + (9.6 x weight in kg) + (1.85 x height in cm) – (4.7 x age in years)
Women	Imperial	BMR = 655 + (4.4 x weight in pounds) + (4.7 x height in inches) - (4.7 x age in years)

Sally needs:

2,150 calories (to maintain weight, answer from Step 2)

- 500 calories (for one pound of weight loss per week)

1,650 (calories needed a day to lose one pound per week)

Sally's Answer to Step 3 = 1,650 calories

If you want to lose 2 pounds a week and DO NOT plan on increasing your exercise, you may subtract 1,000 calories from your answer in Step 2 instead of just 500 calories. You may do this only if subtracting the 1,000 calories does NOT drop your total calories to a number smaller than your answer in Step 1. Under no circumstances should you consume a calorie level below your answer in Step 1. Doing so will lower your metabolic rate. Let's look at Sue, Sally's sister, for what this looks like. To thoroughly understand where the numbers came from, Steps 1, 2, and 3 are provided on the following page for Sue.

Step 1 – Determine How Many Calories Are Needed

Example: Sue

Woman - Sue

50 years old

5' 8" = 68 inches

160 pounds

Imperial Formula

BMR = 655 + (4.4 x weight in pounds) + (4.7 x height in inches) - (4.7 x age in years)

BMR = 655 + (4.4 x 160 pounds) + (4.7 x 68 inches) - (4.7 x 50 years)

BMR = 655 + (704) + (320) - (235)

Sue's Answer to Step 1 (Using the Imperial Formula) = 1,444 calories

Step 2 – Determine Activity Factor

Example: Sue

1,444	X	1.2	=	1,733
(Sue's BMR from Step 1)		(Activity Factor)		(Calories needed to maintain weight)

Sue's Answer to Step 2 = 1,733 calories

Step 3 – Determine Calorie Deductions for Weight Loss

Example: Sue

1,733 calories

- 1,000 calories (in order to lose 2 pounds a week)

---

733 calories

Sue's Answer to Step 3 = 733 calories

You are probably thinking right now, "I'm glad I'm not Sue." Indeed, 723 calories is too low of a calorie level for Sue, or any adult for that matter. If she consumes only 723 calories, she is going to be starving and unable to stay on the diet, and her metabolic rate is going to drop in an attempt to conserve energy. In other words, if Sue only eats 723 calories a day, that number is below 1,444 (her Basal Metabolic Rate, the answer from Step 1). In Sue's case, even if only 500 calories instead of 1,000 are subtracted, the result would be 1,233, which is still below her answer to Step 1.

1,733 – 500 = 1,233 calories

So, what do we do with Sue? First, we want to encourage her to start exercising more so we can use a larger activity factor than 1.2. But if she refuses to exercise, she should consume 1,444 calories. Consuming 1,444 will decrease her risk of stripping lean tissue while she diets and prevent a lowering of her metabolic rate. Importantly, she must be willing to lose less than 1 pound a week. Without exercise, her weight loss will be slowed.

On the other hand, if Sue is willing to increase her activity level, even a little bit, she could safely lose 1 pound a week, as is shown below.

1,444	X	1.375	=	1,986 calories
(Sue's answer from Step 1)		(Light exercise level)		(Calories needed to maintain weight)

1,986 – 500 = 1,486 calories (which is higher than 1,444, Sue's number from Step 1)

Enough about Sue. When you subtract 500 calories in Step 3, if your answer is smaller than your answer in Step 1, it means due to your age or small frame, you should not lose 1 pound a week, but should settle for losing less than 1 pound per week. Don't panic! It is okay! I have worked with many short, slightly-built and/or elderly women who fall into this category. It is okay! It simply means a healthy weight loss will appear on the scale at a slower rate for you. But it is still achievable!!! If you subtract the 500 calories, it will eventually slow your metabolic rate and make it more difficult to lose weight. So, don't do it. If you fall into this category, I suggest you eat the number of calories you determined in Step 1. Not everyone should lose 2 pounds a week. Work with your numbers to determine what rate you should strive to lose.

Your Turn: Individualize it with your numbers

In the space below, determine the number of calories you need in order to lose 1 pound a week. Circle your answer. This is your final calorie goal to lose weight.

______________	–	______________	=	______________
(Answer from Step 2)		(either 500 or 1,000 but maybe less)		(Final calorie goal to lose weight)

After doing this exercise, I hope you feel empowered knowing where all the numbers came from and knowing why you chose them. Now you know how many calories you need to lose weight. You also have a good idea if you are shooting to lose ½ or 2 pounds a week and why. The next section explores how many servings are needed from each food group in order to meet your above-determined calorie requirements while also staying within the recommended ranges of macronutrients consumed.

Step 4 – Servings per Calorie Level

Below is a chart depicting how many servings from each food group are needed in order to meet the various calorie needs and macronutrient requirements. In the left-hand column in the table below are the 6 main food groups, which provide the nutrients we need. Across the top of the table are various calorie levels. The rest of the boxes indicate the number of servings needed daily from each food group in order to achieve the desired calorie level.

This step is simple. In the table below, choose the column that comes closest to your circled answer in Step 3 and note the number of servings from each food group you need each day.

Exchanges for Each Calorie Level

Food Group	1,400 Calories	1,500 Calories	1,600 Calories	1,700 Calories	1,800 Calories	1,900 Calories	2,000 Calories
Low-fat dairy	2	3	3	3	3	3	3
Low to medium fat protein	5	5	5	5	5	5	5.5
Starches	7	7	8	9	9	9	10
Fruit	2	2	2	2	3	4	4
Non-starchy vegetables	3	3	3	4	4	5	5
Fat	2	2	3	3	4	4	4

Step 5 – Your Personal Omega-Z Diet Plan

The ultimate goal of the Omega-Z Diet Plan is autonomy and success for each dieter. Autonomy comes when you are educated, informed, self-reliant, and confident. Success comes from making the right choices, day after day. These charts are followed by some sample menus for each of the calorie levels in order to give you an idea of what kinds of food to eat and how much should be eaten each day. The sample menus are provided as examples, but with the Omega-Z Diet Plan, the choices are nearly endless. Here is the key to the Omega-Z Diet Plan.

The Omega-Z Diet System provides food symbols to represent the 6 major food groups: Starch, Meat, Milk, Vegetables, Fruit, and Fats. While Alcohol is not a food group and is not needed by the body, it is represented because it provides calories that can hinder weight loss. The Omega-Z Diet System Key below depicts two symbols for each food group. One is a full serving, shown on the left, the other is half a serving, shown in the far-right column. These symbols identify each food group. Each calorie level indicates the number of items in each food group that must be consumed and to which you are advised to limit yourself if losing weight.

Starch		½ Starch	
Low-fat Meat		½ Low-fat Meat	
Medium-fat Meat		½ Medium-fat Meat	
High-fat Meat		½ High-fat Meat	
Skim Milk		½ Skim Milk	
Medium-fat Milk 1-2%		½ Medium-fat Milk 1-2%	
High-fat Milk		½ High-fat Milk	
Vegetable		½ Vegetable	
Fruit		½ Fruit	
Fat		½ Fat	
Alcohol		½ Alcohol	
Water		½ Water	

Foods on the Omega–Z list are grouped according to similarity. They are grouped by how many calories they provide and from where those calories come. In other words, foods in each category provide approximately the same number of calories, and grams of carbohydrates, proteins, and fat. So, for example, because both bread and corn contribute a significant amount of carbohydrates, a small amount of protein, and a tiny amount of fat, they are both included in the starch list. Even though most of us have always thought of corn as a vegetable, it will not be found on the vegetable list. Both corn and bread can be found on the starch list. The more familiar you become with the foods you often eat, the more comfort and ease you will experience when looking them up on the Omega-Z list. Because foods provide different vitamins, minerals, and phytochemicals, choosing different foods from within each main category is recommended.

To personalize your plan, simply choose foods from the Omega-Z Food List according to the number of servings recommended from each group for your calorie level.

For example, if you are on the 1,600-calorie diet plan, each day you need to eat:

Omega Z Food Group	# of daily servings	Number of servings PER DAY shown as icons
Starch	8	
Meat	5	
Milk	3	
Fruit	2	
Vegetable	3	
Fat	3	

For breakfast, you might decide you want:

Food Option	Equates To...
⅔ cup plain yogurt	
1¼ cups strawberries	
½ cup orange juice	
½ cup skim milk	
½ cup shredded wheat cereal	
1 cup black coffee	nothing - it is a free food

For lunch, you might have:

Food Option	Equates To...
2 oz. roasted turkey	
½ cup corn	
1 cup broccoli	
½ cup skim milk	
Fresh spinach salad with cucumbers, radishes & red onion	nothing - it is a free food
2 Tbsp reduced-calorie salad dressing	

That means for the rest of the day, between snacks and dinner, the following must be consumed in order to fuel your body properly:

The serving sizes in the left-hand column for each food in the above breakfast and lunch menu (⅔ cup plain yogurt, 1¼ cups strawberries, etc...) came from the Omega-Z Food List. In other words, by looking up foods on the Omega-Z list, you will know how much to consume (or limit yourself to) to fulfill each of the food icons.

Simply choose foods from the Omega-Z Food List (on page 25) until all your servings for the day from each food group have been consumed.

- Spread meals out throughout the day and don't eat everything in a short period of a few hours.
- Record food consumed to help you keep track.
- Choose a variety of foods from within each food group to avoid boredom and ensure adequate vitamins and minerals are provided.
- It is initially important to familiarize yourself with portion sizes. This may require measuring and weighing foods in the beginning until your eye becomes trained to recognize portion sizes.

Please note:

The 3 meat categories are low-fat meat , medium-fat meat and high-fat meat . You have the freedom to choose foods from all 3 categories, but it is recommended you choose mostly from the low-fat meat group. Foods in the high-fat meat group should be consumed sparingly. The more often you choose from the low-fat meat group, the more consistently weight loss can be expected. This flexibility allows for special occasions, eating out, and treats.

The milk categories are similar to the meat categories in that there are 3 categories based on fat content. The 3 milk categories are low-fat milk , medium-fat milk , and high-fat milk . Again, you have freedom to choose foods from all 3 categories, but it is recommended you choose mostly from the low-fat milk group. Foods in the high-fat milk group should be consumed sparingly. The more often you choose from the low-fat milk group, the more consistently you will experience weight loss. But again, the Omega-Z Diet Plan allows for flexibility in an ever-changing world.

RECAP:

Foods on the Omega-Z list are grouped according to similarity regarding what macronutrients they provide for the body.

Choose a variety of foods from within each food group.

From the milk category, choose mostly low-fat milk items.

From the meat category, choose mostly low-fat meats.

Measure and weigh foods to start, until your eye becomes trained to Omega-Z portion sizes.

Track what you have eaten throughout the day to monitor progress.

Omega-Z Food List

Each provides approximately: 80 calories, 15 grams of carbohydrates, 3 grams of protein, and 1 gram of fat.

Each provides approximately: 45 calories and 5 grams of fat.

Each provides approximately: 60 calories and 15 grams of carbohydrates.

Each provides approximately: 25 calories, 5 grams of carbohydrate, and 2 grams of protein.

Each provides approximately: 45 calories, 7 grams of protein, and 2 grams of fat.

Each provides approximately: 75 calories, 7 grams of protein, and 5 grams of fat.

Each provides approximately: 100 calories, 7 grams of protein, and 8 grams of fat.

Each provides approximately: 80 calories, 12 grams of carbohydrate, 8 grams of protein.

Each provides approximately: 125 calories, 12 grams of carbohydrates, 8 grams of protein, and 5 grams of fat.

Each provides approximately: 150 calories, 12 grams of carbohydrates, 8 grams of protein, and 8 grams of fat.

Each provides approximately: 125-150 calories and 5-15 grams of carbohydrates.

STARCHES:

Starches	Serving Size	Omega-Z Food List
Bread		
Bagel, Large	1	
Biscuit	1	
Reduced Calorie	2 slices	
White, Whole-grain, Pumpernickel, Rye	2 slices	
Unfrosted Raisin or Cinnamon	1 slice	
Chapatti or Roti, small, 6 in. across	1	
Naan, 8″ x 2″	1	
Cornbread, 1¾ in. cube	1	
English Muffin	1	
Hot dog/ Hamburger Bun	1	
Pancake	1 Pancake (4″ across, ¼″ thick)	
Pita, 6″ diameter	1	
Roll, plain, small	1	
Stuffing bread	⅓ cup	
Taco shell, hard, 5″ diameter	2	
Torilla, corn, 6″ diameter	1	
Torilla, flour, 10″ diameter	1	
Waffles, 4″ square or 4″ across	1	
Croutons	½ cup	
Cereals and Grains		
Amaranth or Chinese Spinach	⅓ cup	
Barley, cooked	1 cup	
Bran, Dry		
Wheat	½ cup	
Bulgur, cooked	½ cup	

Starches	Serving Size	Omega-Z Food List
Cereals		
Bran	½ cup	
Cooked (Oats, Oatmeal)	1 cup	
Puffed	1½ cup	
Shredded wheat, plain	½ cup	
Sugar-coated	½ cup	
Unsweetened, ready-to-eat	¾ cup	
Couscous	1 cup	
Granola		
Low-fat	¼ cup	
Regular	¼ cup	
Grits, cooked	1 cup	
Kasha	½ cup	
Millet, cooked	⅓ cup	
Muesli	¼ cup	
Pasta, cooked	1 cup	
Polenta, cooked	⅓ cup	
Quinoa, cooked	1 cup	
Rice, white or brown, cooked	1 cup	
Tabbouleh, prepared	½ cup	
Wheat germ, dry	3 Tbsp	
Wild rice, cooked	1 cup	
Starchy Vegetables		
Breadfruit	¼ cup	
Cassava	⅓ cup	
Corn	½ cup	

STARCHES, CONTINUED:

Starches	Serving Size	Omega-Z Food List
Corn on cob	Small (6")	
Hominy, canned	¾ cup	
Mixed vegetables w/ corn, peas, or pasta	1 cup	
Parsnips	½ cup	
Peas, green	½ cup	
Plantain, ripe	½ small (4")	
Potato		
Baked with skin	1 large	
Boiled, all kinds	½ cup or ½ medium potato	
Mashed, with milk and fat	½ cup	
French fried (oven-baked)	1 cup (2 oz)	
Pumpkin, canned, no sugar added	1 cup	
Spaghetti/pasta sauce	½ cup	
Squash, winter (Acorn, Butternut)	1 cup	
Succotash	½ cup	
Yam, Sweet Potato, plain	½ cup	
Crackers		
Animal crackers	16	
Round-butter type	6	
Saltine type	6	
Sandwich-style, cheese, or peanut butter filling	6	
Whole-wheat regular	5	
Whole-wheat lower fat or crispbreads	5	
Graham cracker, 2½"	3	
Granola or snack bar, regular or low fat	1 bar	

Starches	Serving Size	Omega-Z Food List
Matzoh	7 crackers	
Melba toast, about 2x4" piece	5 pieces	
Oyster crackers	20	
Popcorn (air popped without butter)	3 cups	
Pretzels	1 cup	
Snack Chips		
Fat-free or baked (tortilla, potato)	15-20	
Regular (tortilla, potato)	9-13	
Trail Mix		
Candy/nut based	1 oz	
Dried fruit-based	1 oz	

MEATS:

Meat	Serving Size	Omega-Z Food List
Lean Meat		
Beef: trimmed of fat (90% lean); ground, round, roast (chuck, rib, rump), sirloin, steak (cubed, flank, porterhouse, T-bone), tenderloin	1 oz	
Beef jerky	1 oz	
Egg substitutes, plain	¼ cup	
Egg whites	2	
Fish, plain: catfish, cod, flounder, haddock, halibut, orange roughy, salmon, tilapia, trout, tuna	1 oz	
Fish, smoked: herring or salmon (lox)	1 oz	
Game: buffalo, ostrich, rabbit, venison	1 oz	
Hot dog with 3 grams of fat or less per ounce (8 dogs per 14-oz package)	1 oz	
Lamb: chop, leg, or roast	1 oz	
Organ meat: heart, kidney, liver	1 oz	
Oysters, fresh or frozen	6 medium	
Pork, lean		
Canadian bacon	1 oz	
Rib or loin chop/roast, ham, tenderloin	1 oz	
Poultry, without skin: chicken, Cornish Hen, domestic duck or goose (well drained of fat), turkey, lean ground turkey or chicken	1 oz	

Meat	Serving Size	Omega-Z Food List
Processed sandwich meats with 3 grams of fat or less per ounce: chipped beef, deli thin-sliced meats, turkey ham, turkey kielbasa, turkey pastrami	1 oz	
Sausage with 3 grams of fat or less per ounce	1 oz	
Shellfish: clams, crab, imitation shellfish, lobster	1 oz	
Veal, cutlet (no breading), loin chop roast	1 oz	
Shrimp	12 medium size	
Medium-Fat Meat		
Beef: (85% lean) corned, ground meatloaf, prime grades, prime rib (trimmed of fat), short ribs, tongue	1 oz	
Egg	1	
Fish, any fried product	1 oz	
Lamb: ground, rib, roast	1 oz	
Pork: cutlet, shoulder roast	1 oz	
Poultry, with skin: chicken, dove, pheasant, wild duck or goose, fried chicken, ground turkey	1 oz	
Sausage with 4-7 grams of fat per ounce	1 oz	
High-Fat Meat		
Bacon		
Pork	2 slices (1 oz each)	
Turkey	3 slices (½ oz each before cooking)	

MEATS, CONTINUED:

Meat	Serving Size	Omega-Z Food List
Hot Dog		
Beef, pork, combo	1 oz	
Pork: ground, sausage, spareribs	1 oz	
Processed sandwich meats with 8 grams of fat or more per ounce: bologna, hard salami, pastrami	1 oz	
Sausage with 8 grams fat or more per ounce: bratwurst, chorizo, Italian, knockwurst, Polish, smoked summer	1 oz	
Plant-Based Proteins		
"Bacon" strips, soy-based	3 strips	
Baked beans	⅓ cup	
Beans, cooked: black, garbanzo, kidney, lima, navy, pinto, white	½ cup	
"Beef" or "sausage" crumbles, soy-based	2 oz	
"Chicken" nuggets, soy-based	4 nuggets	
Edamame	½ cup	
Falafel (spiced with chickpeas and wheat patties)	3 patties (2" across)	
Hummus	⅓ cup	
Lentils, cooked (brown, green, yellow)	½ cup	
Meatless burger, soy-based	3 oz	
Meatless burger, vegetable and starch based	1 patty (2.5 oz)	
Meatless deli slices	1 oz	
Mycoprotein ("chicken" tenders or crumbles), meatless	2 oz	
Peas, cooked (black-eyed, split)	½ cup	
Refined beans, canned	½ cup	

Meat	Serving Size	Omega-Z Food List
"Sausage" breakfast-type patties, meatless	1 (1.5 oz)	
Tempeh, plain, unflavored	¼ cup	
Tofu	½ cup	
Tofu, light	½ cup	

MILK AND OTHER DAIRY:

Milk	Serving Size	Omega-Z Food List
Skim and Low Fat (1%)		
Milk, buttermilk, acidophilus milk, lactaid	1 cup	
Evaporated milk	½ cup	
Yogurt, plain	⅔ cup	
Reduced-fat (2%)		
Milk, acidophilus milk, kefir, lactaid	1 cup	
Yogurt, plain	⅔ cup	
Whole		
Milk, buttermilk, goat's milk	1 cup	
Evaporated milk	½ cup	
Yogurt, plain	8 oz	
Dairy-Like Foods		
Almond Milk		
Unsweetened	1 cup	
Unsweetened, vanilla	1 cup	
Vanilla	1 cup	
Chocolate Milk		
Skim	1 cup	
Whole	1 cup	
Coconut milk, canned, thick		
Light	⅓ cup	
Regular	3 Tbsp	
Coconut Milk Beverage, thin		
Unsweetened	1 cup	
Coffee Creamer		
Dry, flavored	4 tsp	
Liquid, flavored	2 Tbsp	

Milk	Serving Size	Omega-Z Food List
Cream		
Half and Half	2 Tbsp	
Heavy	1 Tbsp	
Light	1½ Tbsp	
Whipped	2 Tbsp	
Whipped, pressurized	¼ cup	
Eggnog, whole milk	1 cup	
Hot Chocolate		
Regular	1 envelope, water	
Sugar-free or light	1 envelope, water	
Rice Drink		
Flavored, low-fat	1 cup	
Plain, fat-free	1 cup	
Soy Milk		
Light	1 cup	
Regular, plain	1 cup	
Sour Cream		
Reduced fat or light	3 Tbsp	
Regular	2 Tbsp	
Yogurt		
With fruit, low-fat	⅔ cup	
Cheeses		
Cheeses with 3 grams of fat or less per ounce	1 oz	
Cheeses with 4-7 grams of fat per ounce		
Cheese spread	2 Tbsp	
Feta	1 oz/ ¼ cup	
Mozzarella	1 oz	
Reduced-fat cheese	1 oz	

MILK AND OTHER DAIRY, CONTINUED:

Milk	Serving Size	Omega-Z Food List
String	1 oz	
Cheese, regular		
American	1 oz	
Bleu	1 oz	
Brie	1 oz	
Cheddar	1 oz	
Hard Goat	1 oz	
Monterey Jack	1 oz	
Queso	1 oz	
Swiss	1 oz	
Parmesan	4 Tbsp	
Cottage cheese	½ cup	
Cream Cheese		
Reduced-fat	3 Tbsp	
Regular	1 Tbsp	
Ricotta Cheese		
Fat-free, light	¼ cup	
Regular	¼ cup	

FRUIT:

Fruit	Serving Size	Omega-Z Food List
Apple, unpeeled, small	1 whole (4 oz)	
Apples, dried	4 rings	
Applesauce, unsweetened	½ cup	
Apricots		
Canned	½ cup	
Dried	8 halves	
Fresh	4 whole	
Blackberries	¾ cup	
Blueberries	¾ cup	
Cantaloupe, small	1 cup, cubed	
Cherries		
Sweet, canned	½ cup	
Sweet, fresh	12	
Dates	3	
Dried fruits (blackberries, cherries, mixed fruit, raisins)	2 Tbsp	
Figs		
Dried	3	
Fresh	3 large	
Fruit cocktail	½ cup	
Grapefruit		
Large	½	
Sections, canned	¾ cup	
Grapes, small	17 (3 oz)	
Honeydew melon	1 cup cubed	
Kiwi	1	
Loquat	¾ cup cubed	
Mandarin oranges, canned	¾ cup	

FRUIT, CONTINUED:

Fruit	Serving Size	Omega-Z Food List
Mango, small	1	
Nectarine, small	1	
Orange, small	1	
Papaya	1	
Peaches		
Canned	½ cup	
Fresh, large	1	
Pears		
Canned	½ cup	
Fresh, large	1	
Pineapple		
Canned	½ cup	
Fresh	¾ cup	
Plums		
Canned	½ cup	
Dried, prunes	3	
Fresh, small	2	
Pomegranate seeds	⅓ cup	
Raspberries	1 cup	
Strawberries	1¼ cup	
Tangerines, small	2	
Watermelon	1¼ cup cubed	
Banana	Whole 6-7"	
Dried cranberries	2 Tbsp	
Fresh cranberries	1⅓ cup	
Fruit Juice		
Apple juice/cider	½ cup	
Cranberry cocktail	½ cup	

Fruit	Serving Size	Omega-Z Food List
Fruit juice blends, 100% juice	⅓ cup	
Fruit drink, low juice content	1 cup	
Grape juice	⅓ cup	
Grapefruit juice	½ cup	
Lemonade	1 cup	
Orange juice	½ cup	
Pineapple juice	½ cup	
Prune juice	⅓ cup	

VEGETABLES:

Vegetables	Serving Size	Omega-Z Food List
Non-starchy Vegetables		
Artichoke	½ cup	
Artichoke hearts	½ cup	
Asparagus	½ cup	
Bamboo shoots	½ cup	
Beans (green, wax, Italian)	½ cup	
Bean sprouts	½ cup	
Beets	½ cup	
Borscht	½ cup	
Broccoli	½ cup	
Brussels sprouts	½ cup	
Carrots	½ cup	
Cauliflower	½ cup	
Chayote	½ cup	
Coleslaw, packaged, no dressing	½ cup	
Daikon	½ cup	
Eggplant	½ cup	
Fennel	½ cup	
Gourds (bitter, bottle, luffa)	½ cup	
Hearts of palm	½ cup	
Jicama	½ cup	
Kohlrabi	½ cup	
Leeks	½ cup	
Mixed vegetables (without corn, peas, or pasta)	½ cup	
Mung bean sprouts	½ cup	
Mushrooms, all kinds, fresh	½ cup	
Okra	½ cup	
Pea pods	½ cup	
Peppers (all varieties)	½ cup	
Rutabaga	½ cup	
Sauerkraut	½ cup	
Soybean sprouts	½ cup	
Squash (summer, crookneck, zucchini)	½ cup	
Sugar pea snaps	½ cup	
Swiss chard	½ cup	
Tomato	½ cup	
Tomatoes, canned	½ cup	
Tomato/vegetable juice	½ cup	
Marinara Sauce	⅓ cup	
Turnips	½ cup	
Water chestnuts	½ cup	
Yard-long beans	½ cup	
Free Vegetables		
Cabbage (green, bok choy, Chinese)		
Celery		
Cucumber		
Green onions or scallions		
Greens (collard, dandelion, mustard, turnip)		
Kale		
Lettuce		
Onions		

FATS:

Fats	Serving Size	Omega-Z Food List
Monounsaturated Fats		
Avocado, medium	2 tsp (1 oz)	
Nut butters (trans-fat-free): almond butter, cashew butter, peanut butter (smooth or crunchy)	1 Tbsp	
Nuts		
Almonds	6 nuts	
Brazil	6 nuts	
Cashews	6 nuts	
Hazelnuts	6 nuts	
Macadamia	6 nuts	
Peanuts	10 nuts	
Pecans	4 halves	
Pistachios	16 nuts	
Soy, unsalted	¾ oz	
Oil: canola, olive, peanut	1 tsp	
Olives		
Black	8 large	
Green, stuffed	10 large	
Polyunsaturated Fats		
Margarine: Lower-fat spread, (trans-fat free)	1 Tbsp	
Margarine: stick, tub, squeeze (trans-fat free)	1 tsp	
Nuts		
Pine nuts	1 Tbsp	
Walnuts	4 halves	
Oil: corn, cottonseed, flaxseed, grape seed, safflower, soybean, and sunflower	2 tsp (1 oz)	
Oil: made from soybean and canola - Enova seeds	1 Tbsp	

Fats	Serving Size	Omega-Z Food List
Flaxseed		
Ground	1½ tsp	
Whole	1 Tbsp	
Chia seeds	1 Tbsp	
Pumpkin, sunflower seeds	1 Tbsp	
Sesame seeds	1 Tbsp	
Saturated Fats		
Butter		
Reduced-fat	1 Tbsp	
Stick	1 tsp	
Whipped	2 tsp	
Butter blends made with oil		
Reduced-fat or light	1 Tbsp	
Regular	1½ tsp	
Chitterlings, boiled	2 Tbsp	
Coconut, sweetened, shredded	1½ Tbsp	
Lard	1 tsp	
Oil: coconut, palm, palm kernel	1 tsp	
Salt pork	¼ oz	
Shortening, solid	1 tsp	

BEVERAGES:

Beverages	Serving Size	Omega-Z Food List
Coffee, latte (skim milk)	1 small (12 oz)	
Coffee, mocha (skim milk, no whipped cream)	1 small (12 oz)	
Soft drink (soda), regular	12 oz	
Sports drink	8 oz	
Alcohol		
Beer		
Light (less than 4.5% abv)	12 fl oz	
Regular (about 5% abv)	12 fl oz	
Dark (more than 5.7% abv)	12 fl oz	
Distilled Spirits (80 or 86 proof) Vodka, Rum, Gin, Whiskey, Tequila	1½ fl oz	
Liqueur, Coffee (53 proof)	1 fl oz	
Sake	1 fl oz	
Wine		
Champagne/sparkling	5 fl oz	
Dessert (sherry)	3½ fl oz	
Dry, red, or white (10% abv)	5 fl oz	

CONDIMENTS:

Condiments	Serving Size	Omega-Z Food List
Barbeque sauce	3 Tbsp	
Cranberry sauce, jellied	¼ cup	
Curry sauce	1 oz	
Fruit spread, 100% fruit	1½ Tbsp	
Gravy, canned or bottled	½ cup	
Hoisin sauce	1 Tbsp	
Honey	1 Tbsp	
Maple syrup	1½ Tbsp	
Jam or jelly, regular	1 Tbsp	
Mayonnaise		
Reduced-fat	1 Tbsp	
Regular	1 Tbsp	
Mayonnaise-style salad dressing		
Reduced-fat	1 Tbsp	
Regular	2 Tbsp	
Plum sauce	1 Tbsp	
Salad Dressing		
Reduced-calorie	2 Tbsp	
Regular	1 Tbsp	
Mayonnaise-type, reduced-calorie	1 Tbsp	
Mayonnaise-type, regular	1 Tbsp	
Low-calorie	2 Tbsp	Free food
Sweet and sour sauce	3 Tbsp	
Sugar	1 Tbsp	
Syrup		
Chocolate	2 Tbsp	
Light (pancake type)	2 Tbsp	
Regular (pancake type)	1 Tbsp	
Tahini or sesame paste	1 tsp	

DESSERTS:

Dessert	Serving Size	Omega-Z Food List
Banana nut bread	1" slice (1 oz)	
Biscotti	1 oz	
Brownie, small, unfrosted	2 ½" square, ⅞" high	
Cake		
Angel food, unfrosted	1⁄12 of cake (2 oz)	
Frosted	2" square (2 oz)	
Unfrosted	2" square (2 oz)	
Candy bar, chocolate/peanut	2 "fun size" bars	
Candy, hard	3 pieces	
Chocolate "kisses"	5 pieces	
Cookies		
Chocolate chip	2 cookies (2¼" across)	
Gingersnap	3 cookies	
Sandwich, with crème filling	4 small	
Sugar-free	2 small or 1 large	
Vanilla wafer	5 cookies	
Cupcake, frosted	1 small (1¾ oz)	
Danish	1 (2½ oz)	
Doughnut		
Cake, plain	1 medium (1½ oz)	
Yeast type, glazed	3¾" across (2 oz)	
Flan	½ cup	
Frozen pop	1	
Fruit cobbler	½ cup	
Fruit juice bars, frozen, 100% juice	1 bar	
Gelatin, regular	½ cup	

Dessert	Serving Size	Omega-Z Food List
Ice cream		
Fat-free	1 cup	
Light	1 cup	
No sugar added	1 cup	
Regular	1 cup	
Soft serve, with cone	1 small	
Milkshake, any flavor	1 small (12 oz)	
	1 medium (16 oz)	
	1 large (22 oz)	
Muffin (4 oz)	1 muffin	
Pie		
Commerically prepared fruit, two crusts	⅙ of 8" pie	
Pumpkin or custard	⅙ of 8" pie	
Pudding		
Regular (made with 2% milk)	½ cup	
Sugar-free or sugar and fat-free (made with skim milk)	½ cup	
Sherbet, sorbet	1 cup	
Sweet roll	1 (2.5 oz)	
Yogurt, frozen		
Fat-free	1 cup	
Regular	1 cup	
Greek, lower fat, or fat free	1 cup	

COMBINATION FOODS:

Combination Foods	Serving Size	Omega-Z Food List
Entrees		
Burrito (beef and bean)	1 burrito	
Casserole (tuna noodle, lasagna, spaghetti with meatball, chili with beans, macaroni and cheese)	1 cup	
Pizza		
Cheese/vegetarian, thin crust	¼ of 12" pizza	
Meat topping, thin crust	¼ of 12" pizza	
Cheese/ vegetarian or meat topping, rising crust	⅙ of 12" pizza	
Pocket sandwich	1 sandwich	
Pot pie	1 pot pie	
Stews (beef/other meats and vegetables)	1 cup	
Salads (Deli-style)		
Coleslaw	½ cup	
Macaroni/ pasta salad	½ cup	
Tuna or chicken salad	½ cup	
Soups		
Beans, lentil, or split pea soup	1 cup	
Chowder (made with milk)	1 cup	
Cream soup (made with water)	1 cup	
Miso soup	1 cup	
Ramen noodle soup	1 cup	
Rice soup/porridge	1 cup	
Tomato soup (made with water), borscht	1 cup	
Vegetable beef, chicken noodle, or other broth type soup	1 cup	

FAST FOOD:

Fast Foods	Serving Size	Omega-Z Food List
Entrees		
Chicken		
Breast, breaded and fried	1 (7 oz)	
Breast, meat only	1	
Drumstick, breaded and fried	1 (2.5 oz)	
Drumstick, meat only	1	
Nuggets or tender	6 (3.5 oz)	
Thigh, breaded and fried	1 (5 oz)	
Thigh, meat only	1	
Wing, breaded and fried	1 wing	
Main dish salad (grilled chicken-type, no dressing, no croutons)	1 salad (11.5 oz)	
Pizza		
Cheese, pepperoni, or sausage, regular or thick crust	⅛ of a 14" pizza	
Cheese, pepperoni, or sausage, thin crust	⅛ of a 14" pizza	
Cheese, meat, and vegetable, regular crust	⅛ of a 14" pizza	
Asian		
Beef/chicken/shrimp w/vegetables in sauce	1 cup	
Egg roll, meat	1	
Fried rice, meatless	1 cup	
Fortune cookies	1	
Hot-and-sour soup	1 cup	
Meat with sweet sauce	1 cup	
Noodles and vegetables in sauce	1 cup	
Mexican		
Burrito with beans and cheese	1 small (6 oz)	
Nachos with cheese	1 small (about 8 chips)	

FAST FOOD CONTINUED:

Fast Foods	Serving Size	Omega-Z Food List
Mexican Cont.		
Quesadilla, cheese only	1 small (5 oz)	
Taco, crisp, w/ meat and cheese	1 small taco	
Taco salad w/ chicken and tortilla bowl	1 salad (1 lb)	
Tostada with beans and cheese	1 small tostada	
Breakfast Sandwiches		
Breakfast burrito with sausage, egg, and cheese	1 burrito	
Egg, cheese, meat on an English muffin	1 sandwich	
Egg, cheese, meat, on a biscuit	1 sandwich	
Sausage biscuit sandwich	1 sandwich	
Chicken Sandwiches		
Grilled with bun, lettuce, tomato, spread	1 (7.5 oz)	
Crispy with bun, lettuce, tomato, spread	1 (6 oz)	
Fish sandwich with tartar sauce and cheese	1 (5 oz)	
Hamburger		
Regular with bun, ketchup, mustard, onion, and pickle	½ cup	
4 oz meat with cheese, bun, ketchup, mustard, onion, pickle	½ cup	
Hot dog with bun, plain	1 (3.5 oz)	
Submarine Sandwich (no cheese or sauce)		
Less than 6g fat	6" sub	
Regular	6" sub	
Wrap, grilled chicken, vegetables, cheese, and spread	1 small (4-5 oz)	

Fast Foods	Serving Size	Omega-Z Food List
Sides/Appetizers		
French fries	1 small order (3.5 oz)	
	1 medium order (5 oz)	
	1 large order (6 oz)	
Hashbrowns	1 cup/medium order (5 oz)	
Onion rings	8-9 rings (4 oz)	
Salad, side (no dressing, croutons, or cheese)	1 small salad	

Templates for Tracking Food

To assist you in tracking food while on the Omega-Z Diet Plan, the following templates for each calorie level are provided. Simply mark off food groups as they are consumed. Space is also provided for additional information.

Omega-Z Food Diary Template for 1,400 Calories

Date of Food Record ________________ Day of Week ______________________

Omega-Z Food Group	# of Daily Servings	# of servings PER DAY as shown by icons
Starch	7	
Meat	5	
Milk	2	
Fruit	2	
Vegetable	3	
Fat	2	
Water	Women: 9 Men: 13	Women: Men:

Breakfast:

When:

Where:

With Whom:

Activity while Eating:

Reason for Choice:

Length of Meal:

Degree of Hunger Before: High Medium Low

Degree of Satisfaction After: High Medium Low

If you have identified that you are an emotional eater, please comment on how you felt before, during, and after the meal:

____

____

Lunch:

When:

Where:

With Whom:

Activity while Eating:

Reason for Choice:

Length of Meal:

Degree of Hunger Before: High Medium Low

Degree of Satisfaction After: High Medium Low

If you have identified that you are an emotional eater, please comment on how you felt before, during, and after the meal:

____

____

Dinner:

When:

Where:

With Whom:

Activity while Eating:

Reason for Choice:

Length of Meal:

Degree of Hunger Before: High Medium Low

Degree of Satisfaction After: High Medium Low

If you have identified that you are an emotional eater, please comment on how you felt before, during, and after the meal:

____

____

Snack:

When:

Where:

With Whom:

Activity while Eating:

Reason for Choice:

Length of Meal:

Degree of Hunger Before: High Medium Low

Degree of Satisfaction After: High Medium Low

If you have identified that you are an emotional eater, please comment on how you felt before, during, and after the meal:

____

____

Snack:

When:

Where:

With Whom:

Activity while Eating:

Reason for Choice:

Length of Meal:

Degree of Hunger Before: High Medium Low

Degree of Satisfaction After: High Medium Low

If you have identified that you are an emotional eater, please comment on how you felt before, during, and after the meal:

____

____

Snack:

When:

Where:

With Whom:

Activity while Eating:

Reason for Choice:

Length of Meal:

Degree of Hunger Before: High Medium Low

Degree of Satisfaction After: High Medium Low

If you have identified that you are an emotional eater, please comment on how you felt before, during, and after the meal:

____

____

Omega-Z Food Diary Template for 1,500 Calories

Date of Food Record ________________ Day of Week ______________________

Omega-Z Food Group	# of Daily Servings	# of servings PER DAY as shown by icons
Starch	7	
Meat	5	
Milk	3	
Fruit	2	
Vegetable	3	
Fat	2	
Water	Women: 9 Men: 13	Women: Men:

Breakfast:

When:

Where:

With Whom:

Activity while Eating:

Reason for Choice:

Length of Meal:

Degree of Hunger Before: High Medium Low

Degree of Satisfaction After: High Medium Low

If you have identified that you are an emotional eater, please comment on how you felt before, during, and after the meal:

____

____

Lunch:

When:

Where:

With Whom:

Activity while Eating:

Reason for Choice:

Length of Meal:

Degree of Hunger Before: High Medium Low

Degree of Satisfaction After: High Medium Low

If you have identified that you are an emotional eater, please comment on how you felt before, during, and after the meal:

____

____

Dinner:

When:

Where:

With Whom:

Activity while Eating:

Reason for Choice:

Length of Meal:

Degree of Hunger Before: High Medium Low

Degree of Satisfaction After: High Medium Low

If you have identified that you are an emotional eater, please comment on how you felt before, during, and after the meal:

____

____

Snack:

When:

Where:

With Whom:

Activity while Eating:

Reason for Choice:

Length of Meal:

Degree of Hunger Before: High Medium Low

Degree of Satisfaction After: High Medium Low

If you have identified that you are an emotional eater, please comment on how you felt before, during, and after the meal:

____

____

Snack:

When:

Where:

With Whom:

Activity while Eating:

Reason for Choice:

Length of Meal:

Degree of Hunger Before: High Medium Low

Degree of Satisfaction After: High Medium Low

If you have identified that you are an emotional eater, please comment on how you felt before, during, and after the meal:

____

____

Snack:

When:

Where:

With Whom:

Activity while Eating:

Reason for Choice:

Length of Meal:

Degree of Hunger Before: High Medium Low

Degree of Satisfaction After: High Medium Low

If you have identified that you are an emotional eater, please comment on how you felt before, during, and after the meal:

____

____

Omega-Z Food Diary Template for 1,600 Calories

Date of Food Record ________________ Day of Week ______________________

Omega-Z Food Group	# of Daily Servings	# of servings PER DAY as shown by icons
Starch	8	
Meat	5	
Milk	3	
Fruit	2	
Vegetable	3	
Fat	3	
Water	Women: 9 Men: 13	Women: Men:

Breakfast:

When:

Where:

With Whom:

Activity while Eating:

Reason for Choice:

Length of Meal:

Degree of Hunger Before: High Medium Low

Degree of Satisfaction After: High Medium Low

If you have identified that you are an emotional eater, please comment on how you felt before, during, and after the meal:

____

____

Lunch:

When:

Where:

With Whom:

Activity while Eating:

Reason for Choice:

Length of Meal:

Degree of Hunger Before: High Medium Low

Degree of Satisfaction After: High Medium Low

If you have identified that you are an emotional eater, please comment on how you felt before, during, and after the meal:

____

____

Dinner:

When:

Where:

With Whom:

Activity while Eating:

Reason for Choice:

Length of Meal:

Degree of Hunger Before: High Medium Low

Degree of Satisfaction After: High Medium Low

If you have identified that you are an emotional eater, please comment on how you felt before, during, and after the meal:

____

____

Snack:

When:

Where:

With Whom:

Activity while Eating:

Reason for Choice:

Length of Meal:

Degree of Hunger Before: High Medium Low

Degree of Satisfaction After: High Medium Low

If you have identified that you are an emotional eater, please comment on how you felt before, during, and after the meal:

____

____

Snack:

When:

Where:

With Whom:

Activity while Eating:

Reason for Choice:

Length of Meal:

Degree of Hunger Before: High Medium Low

Degree of Satisfaction After: High Medium Low

If you have identified that you are an emotional eater, please comment on how you felt before, during, and after the meal:

____

____

Snack:

When:

Where:

With Whom:

Activity while Eating:

Reason for Choice:

Length of Meal:

Degree of Hunger Before: High Medium Low

Degree of Satisfaction After: High Medium Low

If you have identified that you are an emotional eater, please comment on how you felt before, during, and after the meal:

____

____

Omega-Z Food Diary Template for 1,700 Calories

Date of Food Record ________________ Day of Week ______________________

Omega-Z Food Group	# of Daily Servings	# of servings PER DAY as shown by icons
Starch	9	
Meat	5	
Milk	3	
Fruit	2	
Vegetable	4	
Fat	3	
Water	Women: 9 Men: 13	Women: Men:

Breakfast:

When:

Where:

With Whom:

Activity while Eating:

Reason for Choice:

Length of Meal:

Degree of Hunger Before: High Medium Low

Degree of Satisfaction After: High Medium Low

If you have identified that you are an emotional eater, please comment on how you felt before, during, and after the meal:

____

____

Lunch:

When:

Where:

With Whom:

Activity while Eating:

Reason for Choice:

Length of Meal:

Degree of Hunger Before: High Medium Low

Degree of Satisfaction After: High Medium Low

If you have identified that you are an emotional eater, please comment on how you felt before, during, and after the meal:

____

____

Dinner:

When:

Where:

With Whom:

Activity while Eating:

Reason for Choice:

Length of Meal:

Degree of Hunger Before: High Medium Low

Degree of Satisfaction After: High Medium Low

If you have identified that you are an emotional eater, please comment on how you felt before, during, and after the meal:

____

____

Snack:

When:

Where:

With Whom:

Activity while Eating:

Reason for Choice:

Length of Meal:

Degree of Hunger Before: High Medium Low

Degree of Satisfaction After: High Medium Low

If you have identified that you are an emotional eater, please comment on how you felt before, during, and after the meal:

____

____

Snack:

When:

Where:

With Whom:

Activity while Eating:

Reason for Choice:

Length of Meal:

Degree of Hunger Before: High Medium Low

Degree of Satisfaction After: High Medium Low

If you have identified that you are an emotional eater, please comment on how you felt before, during, and after the meal:

____

____

Snack:

When:

Where:

With Whom:

Activity while Eating:

Reason for Choice:

Length of Meal:

Degree of Hunger Before: High Medium Low

Degree of Satisfaction After: High Medium Low

If you have identified that you are an emotional eater, please comment on how you felt before, during, and after the meal:

____

____

Omega-Z Food Diary Template for 1,800 Calories

Date of Food Record ________________ Day of Week ______________________

Omega-Z Food Group	# of Daily Servings	# of servings PER DAY as shown by icons
Starch	9	
Meat	5	
Milk	3	
Fruit	3	
Vegetable	4	
Fat	4	
Water	Women: 9 Men: 13	Women: Men:

Breakfast:

When:

Where:

With Whom:

Activity while Eating:

Reason for Choice:

Length of Meal:

Degree of Hunger Before: High Medium Low

Degree of Satisfaction After: High Medium Low

If you have identified that you are an emotional eater, please comment on how you felt before, during, and after the meal:

____

____

Lunch:

When:

Where:

With Whom:

Activity while Eating:

Reason for Choice:

Length of Meal:

Degree of Hunger Before: High Medium Low

Degree of Satisfaction After: High Medium Low

If you have identified that you are an emotional eater, please comment on how you felt before, during, and after the meal:

____

____

Dinner:

When:

Where:

With Whom:

Activity while Eating:

Reason for Choice:

Length of Meal:

Degree of Hunger Before: High Medium Low

Degree of Satisfaction After: High Medium Low

If you have identified that you are an emotional eater, please comment on how you felt before, during, and after the meal:

____

____

Snack:

When:

Where:

With Whom:

Activity while Eating:

Reason for Choice:

Length of Meal:

Degree of Hunger Before: High Medium Low

Degree of Satisfaction After: High Medium Low

If you have identified that you are an emotional eater, please comment on how you felt before, during, and after the meal:

____

____

Snack:

When:

Where:

With Whom:

Activity while Eating:

Reason for Choice:

Length of Meal:

Degree of Hunger Before: High Medium Low

Degree of Satisfaction After: High Medium Low

If you have identified that you are an emotional eater, please comment on how you felt before, during, and after the meal:

____

____

Snack:

When:

Where:

With Whom:

Activity while Eating:

Reason for Choice:

Length of Meal:

Degree of Hunger Before: High Medium Low

Degree of Satisfaction After: High Medium Low

If you have identified that you are an emotional eater, please comment on how you felt before, during, and after the meal:

____

____

Omega-Z Food Diary Template for 1,900 Calories

Date of Food Record ________________ Day of Week ______________________

Omega-Z Food Group	# of Daily Servings	# of servings PER DAY as shown by icons
Starch	9	
Meat	5	
Milk	3	
Fruit	4	
Vegetable	5	
Fat	4	
Water	Women: 9 Men: 13	Women: Men:

Breakfast:

When:

Where:

With Whom:

Activity while Eating:

Reason for Choice:

Length of Meal:

Degree of Hunger Before: High Medium Low

Degree of Satisfaction After: High Medium Low

If you have identified that you are an emotional eater, please comment on how you felt before, during, and after the meal:

____

____

Lunch:

When:

Where:

With Whom:

Activity while Eating:

Reason for Choice:

Length of Meal:

Degree of Hunger Before: High Medium Low

Degree of Satisfaction After: High Medium Low

If you have identified that you are an emotional eater, please comment on how you felt before, during, and after the meal:

____

____

Dinner:

When:

Where:

With Whom:

Activity while Eating:

Reason for Choice:

Length of Meal:

Degree of Hunger Before: High Medium Low

Degree of Satisfaction After: High Medium Low

If you have identified that you are an emotional eater, please comment on how you felt before, during, and after the meal:

____

____

Snack:

When:

Where:

With Whom:

Activity while Eating:

Reason for Choice:

Length of Meal:

Degree of Hunger Before: High Medium Low

Degree of Satisfaction After: High Medium Low

If you have identified that you are an emotional eater, please comment on how you felt before, during, and after the meal:

____

____

Snack:

When:

Where:

With Whom:

Activity while Eating:

Reason for Choice:

Length of Meal:

Degree of Hunger Before: High Medium Low

Degree of Satisfaction After: High Medium Low

If you have identified that you are an emotional eater, please comment on how you felt before, during, and after the meal:

____

____

Snack:

When:

Where:

With Whom:

Activity while Eating:

Reason for Choice:

Length of Meal:

Degree of Hunger Before: High Medium Low

Degree of Satisfaction After: High Medium Low

If you have identified that you are an emotional eater, please comment on how you felt before, during, and after the meal:

____

____

Omega-Z Food Diary Template for 2,000 Calories

Date of Food Record ________________ Day of Week ______________________

Omega-Z Food Group	# of Daily Servings	# of servings PER DAY as shown by icons
Starch	10	
Meat	5.5	
Milk	3	
Fruit	4	
Vegetable	5	
Fat	4	
Water	Women: 9 Men: 13	Women: Men:

Breakfast:

When:

Where:

With Whom:

Activity while Eating:

Reason for Choice:

Length of Meal:

Degree of Hunger Before: High Medium Low

Degree of Satisfaction After: High Medium Low

If you have identified that you are an emotional eater, please comment on how you felt before, during, and after the meal:

____

____

Lunch:

When:

Where:

With Whom:

Activity while Eating:

Reason for Choice:

Length of Meal:

Degree of Hunger Before: High Medium Low

Degree of Satisfaction After: High Medium Low

If you have identified that you are an emotional eater, please comment on how you felt before, during, and after the meal:

____

____

Dinner:

When:

Where:

With Whom:

Activity while Eating:

Reason for Choice:

Length of Meal:

Degree of Hunger Before: High Medium Low

Degree of Satisfaction After: High Medium Low

If you have identified that you are an emotional eater, please comment on how you felt before, during, and after the meal:

____

____

Snack:

When:

Where:

With Whom:

Activity while Eating:

Reason for Choice:

Length of Meal:

Degree of Hunger Before: High Medium Low

Degree of Satisfaction After: High Medium Low

If you have identified that you are an emotional eater, please comment on how you felt before, during, and after the meal:

____

____

Snack:

When:

Where:

With Whom:

Activity while Eating:

Reason for Choice:

Length of Meal:

Degree of Hunger Before: High Medium Low

Degree of Satisfaction After: High Medium Low

If you have identified that you are an emotional eater, please comment on how you felt before, during, and after the meal:

____

____

Snack:

When:

Where:

With Whom:

Activity while Eating:

Reason for Choice:

Length of Meal:

Degree of Hunger Before: High Medium Low

Degree of Satisfaction After: High Medium Low

If you have identified that you are an emotional eater, please comment on how you felt before, during, and after the meal:

____

____

Sample Menu Plans

To get you started with the Omega-Z Diet Plan, 3 days of menus are provided for each calorie level. You may notice that, except for skim milk, meals do not include any beverages except water.

While the menus and recipes are designed for their specific calorie levels, they are made from common, everyday foods, not special diet products. Thus, with portion adjustments, they are suitable for sharing with family members. The recipes for many of the meals in the sample menus are included in the back of the workbook. The sample menus and the Omega-Z system are designed to give you an idea of the amount and kinds of foods to be eaten for your calorie level to promote safe and effective long-term weight loss.

1,400-Calorie 3-Day Sample Menu

Omega-Z Food Group	Servings per day
Starch	7
Meat	5
Milk	2
Fruit	2
Vegetable	3
Fat	2

Meal	Day 1	Day 2	Day 3
Breakfast	**Oat Bowl** Black coffee or unsweetened tea	Yogurt Fruit Bowl - ⅔ cup low-fat plain yogurt - 1 Tbsp honey - 1¼ cup strawberries - ¼ cup granola, low fat Black coffee or unsweetened hot tea 8 oz water	**Tropical Smoothie** Black coffee or unsweetened tea
Snack	10-11 baby carrots (½ cup)	1 apple	3 graham crackers
Lunch	12 Saltine crackers Side salad with: 2 oz rotisserie turkey, baby spinach, cucumbers, radishes, watercress, lemon juice, white vinegar and dash lemon seasoning 8 oz water	**Open-Face Chicken and Avocado Tortilla**	1 cup cooked quinoa 1 cup Brussels sprouts, cooked ½ cup roasted corn ½ cup tomatoes 2 cups raw spinach ½ cup edamame beans 2 Tbsp low-calorie dressing 1 cup skim milk
Snack	½ cup fresh blueberries	3 graham crackers 1 cup skim milk	Spinach salad with radishes, cucumbers, and lemon juice dressing
Dinner	**Chicken Stir Fry over Rice** 1 cup milk 8 oz water	**Ground Turkey and Brussels Sprout Salad** 8 oz water	**Black Bean Taco Salad** 8 oz water
Snack		3 cups air-popped popcorn	

*BOLD TYPE indicates recipe is included

Please note: Women should strive to consume about 9 cups of fluid a day and men about 13 cups daily. Some will be consumed with meals, but it is recommended that water also be consumed throughout the day.

1,500-Calorie 3-Day Sample Menu

Omega-Z Food Group	Servings per day
Starch	7
Meat	5
Milk	3
Fruit	2
Vegetable	3
Fat	2

Meal	Day 1	Day 2	Day 3
Breakfast	1 scrambled egg or 2 egg whites with garlic, onion powder, and paprika 2 slices whole wheat bread 3 slices turkey bacon ½ cup orange juice 1 cup skim milk Black coffee or unsweetened tea	½ whole wheat English muffin 2 slices (1 oz total) lean Canadian bacon 1 scrambled egg ½ cup orange juice Black coffee or unsweetened tea	**Green Ginger Smoothie** Black coffee or unsweetened tea
Snack	½ cup bran cereal 1 cup skim milk		
Lunch	**Mustard Tuna Salad with Garlic Mustard Vinaigrette** 8 oz water 1 cup skim milk	2 oz pan-seared salmon 2 cups sautéed spinach 1 cup brown rice ½ cup steamed carrots 1 cup skim milk 8 oz water	2.5 oz grilled turkey breast ⅔ cup cooked quinoa ½ cup red bell pepper 2 Tbsp reduced-calorie Italian dressing ¼ cup feta cheese 1 cup skim milk
Snack		¼ cup blueberries ⅔ cup low-fat yogurt	1 cup skim milk 6 graham crackers
Dinner	1.5 oz ground chicken 1 cup broccoli 1 small sweet potato with cinnamon ½ cup cooked fresh asparagus 8 oz water	1 oz grilled chicken breast 1 large sweet potato with ½ tsp butter 1 Tbsp honey 1 oz assorted nuts (about ¼ tsp butter) 1 Tbsp coconut, dried, shredded 1 cup steamed broccoli 1 cup skim milk	**Chicken and Mushroom Pasta** 8 oz water
Snack			

*BOLD TYPE indicates recipe is included

Please note: Women should strive to consume about 9 cups of fluid a day and men about 13 cups daily. Some will be consumed with meals, but it is recommended that water also be consumed throughout the day.

1,600-Calorie 3-Day Sample Menu

Omega-Z Food Group	Servings per day
Starch	8
Meat	5
Milk	3
Fruit	2
Vegetable	3
Fat	3

Meal	Day 1	Day 2	Day 3
Breakfast	1 scrambled egg 1 cup chopped spinach 2 slices whole wheat bread ½ banana 1 cup skim milk Black coffee or unsweetened tea	**Peach Smoothie** **Scrambled Eggs** Black coffee or unsweetened tea	**Strawberry Smoothie** Black coffee or unsweetened tea
Snack	3 graham crackers 1 cup skim milk		½ bagel with 3 Tbsp low-fat cream cheese
Lunch	**Turkey Swiss Sandwich** ½ cup diced tomatoes, cucumbers, and onion 8 oz water 1 cup skim milk	**Orange Shredded Chicken** 8 oz water	**Grilled Chicken with Garlicked Vegetables** 1 medium baked potato 1 cup skim milk
Snack	8 animal crackers 12 almonds 8 oz water	½ bagel with 1 tsp butter 1 cup skim milk	
Dinner	**Chicken Lettuce Wraps** 8 oz water	**Halibut Steamed with Red Potatoes** 8 oz water	**Chicken Cilantro Quesadilla** 8 oz water 1 cup skim milk
Snack		3 cups air-popped popcorn 1 cup skim milk	

*BOLD TYPE indicates recipe is included

Please note: Women should strive to consume about 9 cups of fluid a day and men about 13 cups daily. Some will be consumed with meals, but it is recommended that water also be consumed throughout the day.

1,700-Calorie 3-Day Sample Menu

Omega-Z Food Group	Servings per day
Starch	9
Meat	5
Milk	3
Fruit	2
Vegetable	4
Fat	3

Meal	Day 1	Day 2	Day 3
Breakfast	**Tropical Smoothie** ½ bagel Black coffee or unsweetened tea	**Beta-Carotene Smoothie** 1 cup Kasha cereal 1 cup skim milk Black coffee or unsweetened tea	**Raspberry Smoothie** ¼ cup low-fat granola ⅔ cup plain yogurt Black coffee or unsweetened tea
Snack	12 animal crackers ½ cup skim milk	16 animal crackers 1 cup skim milk	
Lunch	**Turkey Mac & Cheese with Asparagus** 8 oz water 1 cup skim milk	⅔ cup couscous 2 oz rotisserie-style turkey 2 cups spinach with cucumbers and radishes with lemon and vinegar dressing 1 cup skim milk 8 oz water	**Ham English Muffin** ½ cup baby carrots 8 oz water
Snack		1 Tbsp almond butter Celery stalks	16 animal crackers 1 cup skim milk
Dinner	2 oz skinless chicken breast 1 medium sweet potato with cinnamon Salad of 2 cups spinach greens, ½ cup tomatoes, ½ cup shredded carrots, ½ cup cucumbers, 4 halves of walnuts Dressing: 2 Tbsp regular salad dressing 8 oz water	**Chicken Hemp Salad** 5 whole wheat crackers 8 oz water	**Buttered Salmon with Brussels Sprouts** 8 oz water
Snack			3 cups air-popped popcorn

*BOLD TYPE indicates recipe is included

Please note: Women should strive to consume about 9 cups of fluid a day and men about 13 cups daily. Some will be consumed with meals, but it is recommended that water also be consumed throughout the day.

1,800-Calorie 3-Day Sample Menu

Omega-Z Food Group	Servings per day
Starch	9
Meat	5
Milk	3
Fruit	3
Vegetable	4
Fat	4

Meal	Day 1	Day 2	Day 3
Breakfast	**Tropical Smoothie** ½ cup Kasha cereal with ½ cup skim milk Black coffee or unsweetened tea	**Pineapple Breakfast Smoothie** ½ bagel with ½ Tbsp reduced-fat butter Black coffee or unsweetened tea	**Orange Breakfast Smoothie** ¼ cup low-fat granola ½ cup skim milk Black coffee or unsweetened tea
Snack	6 3" square graham crackers 1 cup skim milk	8 animal crackers 1 cup skim milk	
Lunch	2 oz skinless chicken breast 1 medium sweet potato with cinnamon Salad of 2 cups greens, ½ cup tomatoes, ½ cup shredded carrots, ½ cup cucumbers 4 walnut halves 2 Tbsp reduced-calorie dressing 8 oz water	**Spaghetti Squash Pasta with Basil Pesto** 1 cup green beans 1 cup skim milk 8 oz water	**Turkey and Swiss Sandwich** Salad: 1 cup spinach, radishes, cucumbers with 2 Tbsp low-calorie dressing, and 4 slices of avocado 8 oz water
Snack			16 animal crackers ½ cup skim milk
Dinner	**Turkey Mac & Cheese with Asparagus** 8 oz water	**Lime Beef Tenderloin and Avocado Salad** 1 cup milk 8 oz water	**Smoked Salmon and Vegetables** 8 oz water
Snack	1¼ cup strawberries 2 Tbsp whipped cream	3 cups air-popped popcorn	3 cups air-popped popcorn

*BOLD TYPE indicates recipe is included

Please note: Women should strive to consume about 9 cups of fluid a day and men about 13 cups daily. Some will be consumed with meals, but it is recommended that water also be consumed throughout the day.

1,900-Calorie 3-Day Sample Menu

Omega-Z Food Group	Servings per day
Starch	9
Meat	5
Milk	3
Fruit	4
Vegetable	5
Fat	4

Meal	Day 1	Day 2	Day 3
Breakfast	**Egg White Western Omelet** Herb and Cheese Red Potato Hash 1 cup skim milk Black coffee or unsweetened tea	**Antioxidant Smoothie** Black coffee or unsweetened tea	Oatmeal bowl with: 1 cup oats ⅔ plain low-fat yogurt ¾ cup blueberries ½ banana 1 cup raspberries Black coffee or unsweetened tea
Snack		1 cup oatmeal cereal ⅔ cup low-fat yogurt 1 tsp chocolate chips	8 animal crackers 1 cup skim milk
Lunch	**Black Bean Quesadilla** 1 peach 8 oz water 1 cup skim milk	3 oz grilled chicken 1 small sweet potato ½ cup beets ½ cup cauliflower ½ cup diced summer squash 8 oz water	**Steamed Halibut with Red Potatoes and Asparagus** 8 oz water 1 cup skim milk
Snack	Fruit Bowl: ¾ cup blueberries, 1 kiwi, 1 cup raspberries, ⅔ cup low-fat Greek yogurt, plain	3 graham crackers 1 cup skim milk	1 peach
Dinner	**Quick Shrimp Parmesan** ½ cup steamed broccoli 8 oz water	2 oz pork chop and **Arborio Risotto Rice with Parmesan Cheese** 8 oz water	**Chicken Marsala** 1 cup steamed carrots 8 oz water
Snack			1 cup baby carrots

*BOLD TYPE indicates recipe is included

Please note: Women should strive to consume about 9 cups of fluid a day and men about 13 cups daily. Some will be consumed with meals, but it is recommended that water also be consumed throughout the day.

2,000-Calorie 3-Day Sample Menu

Omega-Z Food Group	Servings per day
Starch	10
Meat	5.5
Milk	3
Fruit	4
Vegetable	5
Fat	4

Meal	Day 1	Day 2	Day 3
Breakfast	**Mango Orange Smoothie** 1 fried egg 1 slice whole wheat bread with melted ½ oz of shredded cheddar cheese Black coffee or unsweetened tea	**Berry Smoothie** ½ bagel with 1½ Tbsp reduced-fat cream cheese Black coffee or unsweetened tea	**Acai Smoothie Bowl** 1 medium egg 1 oz grated cheddar cheese 1 slice whole wheat toast Black coffee or unsweetened tea
Snack	6 almonds		
Lunch	2 oz skinless chicken breast 1 medium (2″ diameter) sweet potato 1 tsp cinnamon, ground 1 cup spinach, cooked from fresh 8 oz water	**Chicken and Vegetable Lunch** 8 oz water	**Chicken and Mushroom Pasta** 1 cup skim milk
Snack	16 animal crackers 1 cup skim milk	6 graham crackers ½ cup skim milk	8 animal crackers 1 cup skim milk
Dinner	**Maple-glazed Salmon Pomegranate Salad** 1 cup milk 8 oz water	**Savory Turkey and Brussels Sprout Salad** 1 cup skim milk 8 oz water	**Salmon and Marinara Orzo Dinner** ½ cup broccoli 1 cup skim milk
Snack	3 cups air-popped popcorn	3 cups air popped-popcorn	

*BOLD TYPE indicates recipe is included

Please note: Women should strive to consume about 9 cups of fluid a day and men about 13 cups daily. Some will be consumed with meals, but it is recommended that water also be consumed throughout the day.

Recipes

Peach Smoothie

INGREDIENTS:

½ cup frozen peaches

½ small banana

1 cup skim milk

2 cups spinach, raw

1 cup spring water

½ tsp cinnamon

INSTRUCTIONS:

In a blender, combine milk and spinach and blend until smooth.

Add frozen peaches, banana, cinnamon, and water, blending again until smooth and creamy.

Serve in a glass.

Icons: 

Antioxidant Smoothie

INGREDIENTS:

1 cup spinach, raw

1¼ cups frozen strawberries

¾ cup blueberries, fresh

1 cup skim milk

1 cup raw kale, chopped

1 whole 7" banana

1 Tbsp honey

1 tsp cinnamon

½ Tbsp almond butter, unsalted

2 cups water

INSTRUCTIONS:

In a blender, combine spinach, milk and kale and blend until smooth.

Once blended, add berries, banana, honey, almond butter, cinnamon, and water and blend again until smooth.

Serve in a glass.

Icons:   

Pineapple Breakfast Smoothie

INGREDIENTS:

2 cups kale, stems removed

2 cups water

1½ cups chopped pineapple chunks, fresh

½ medium banana

1 cup almond milk, unsweetened

1 Tbsp chia seeds

1 Tbsp flax seeds, chopped

1 cup ice (optional)

INSTRUCTIONS:

Blend almond milk and kale in a blender until smooth.

Add pineapple, banana, chia seeds, flax seeds, and the additional water, and blend again until smooth.

Serve in a glass.

Icons:

Acai Smoothie Bowl

INGREDIENTS:

2 cups cut spinach, raw

1 cup coconut milk, plain, unsweetened

1¼ cup frozen strawberries, unsweetened

¾ cup blackberries, raw, whole pieces

¼ cup water

½ cup acai berries

½ medium banana, raw, sliced

9 almonds, raw, chopped

1½ Tbsp shredded coconut, dried, flaked, unsweetened

1 Tbsp chia seeds

¼ cup of oatmeal, regular or quick, dry

1 tsp cinnamon, ground

INSTRUCTIONS:

Blend 2 cups spinach, 1 cup coconut milk, and ¼ cup of oatmeal until smooth.

Add strawberries, blackberries, acai berries and ¼ cup water and blend again until smooth.

Pour into a bowl, then on top of the bowl place the almonds, coconut shreds, chia seeds, cinnamon, and the sliced banana. Enjoy with a spoon or as a smoothie.

Icons: 

Berry Smoothie

INGREDIENTS:

1½ cups blueberries, whole

1¼ cups strawberry halves, raw

1 Tbsp almond butter, unsalted

1 cup whole milk

1 cup spring water

1 cup spinach, raw

½ cup oatmeal, regular, dry

⅓ cup low-fat Greek yogurt, plain

1 tsp cinnamon

½ medium banana, raw

1 Tbsp honey

1 cup ice (optional)

INSTRUCTIONS:

In a blender, add 1 cup spinach, 1½ cups blueberries, 1 cup whole milk, and ice. Blend until smooth.

After blending, add the strawberries, almond butter, oats, Greek yogurt, cinnamon, banana, honey, and 1 cup water, and blend again until smooth.

Serve in a glass.

Icons: 

Beta-Carotene Smoothie

INGREDIENTS:

½ cup frozen peaches

½ small banana

1 cup skim milk

2 cups spinach, raw

1 cup spring water

½ tsp cinnamon

INSTRUCTIONS:

In a blender, combine milk and spinach and blend until smooth.

Add frozen peaches, banana, cinnamon and water, blending again until smooth and creamy.

Serve in a glass.

Icons:

Green Ginger Smoothie

INGREDIENTS:

2 cups spinach

1 cup skim milk or almond milk, plain, unsweetened

¼ cup mango, fresh

¼ small banana, raw

1 Tbsp ginger root, raw

3 Medjool dates

¼ cup water

INSTRUCTIONS:

Blend 2 cups spinach and 1 cup of skim or almond milk in a blender until smooth.

Add the mango, ginger, banana, dates, and the extra water, and blend again until smooth.

If smoothie is too thick for your liking, add more water and blend until desired consistency.

Pour into a cup or glass and enjoy.

Icons: 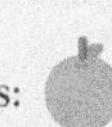  

Green Smoothie

INGREDIENTS:

2 cups kale, raw, chopped

1 cup almond milk, plain, unsweetened; or skim milk

½ banana

1 cup mango, fresh

1 cup spring water

1 Tbsp almond butter, unsalted

1 ¼ cups frozen strawberries, unsweetened

INSTRUCTIONS:

Blend milk and kale in a blender until smooth.

Add banana, mango, almond butter, and frozen strawberries. Blend again for 1–2 minutes or until smooth and green throughout. Add water as needed. Enjoy!

Icons:

Mango Orange Smoothie

INGREDIENTS:

½ cup fresh mango

1 cup spring water

2 cups chopped kale, raw

1 cup carrots, raw

½ cup raw oranges

1 cup skim milk

1 cup ice (optional)

INSTRUCTIONS:

Blend 2 cups kale and 1 cup milk in a blender until smooth.

Add the mango, carrots, oranges, and the cup of water, and blend until smooth.

Serve in a glass.

Icons:

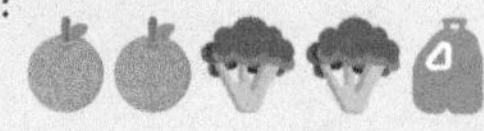

Orange Breakfast Smoothie

INGREDIENTS:

½ cup orange juice, fresh

½ small banana, frozen

¾ cup raw pineapple chunks

1 cup skim milk

⅔ cup plain yogurt

1 tsp vanilla

½ cup spring water

INSTRUCTIONS:

In a blender, blend orange juice and frozen banana. Blend until smooth and not chunky.

Add the pineapple and vanilla, along with yogurt and water, and blend again until smooth and creamy.

Pour into a glass and enjoy.

Icons:

Raspberry Smoothie

INGREDIENTS:

1 cup raspberries, raw

¾ cup blueberries, frozen, unsweetened

1 cup skim milk

1 Tbsp flax seeds

½ Tbsp almond butter

1 cup water

1 cup ice (optional)

INSTRUCTIONS:

Blend 1 cup milk and 1 cup raspberries in a blender until smooth.

Add blueberries, flax seed, almond butter, and 1 cup water.

Blend until smooth; if it is still too thick, add additional water to achieve desired thickness.

Serve in a glass.

Icons:

Strawberry Smoothie

INGREDIENTS:

1¼ cups strawberries, frozen, unsweetened

½ cup mango, fresh

1 Tbsp chia seeds

1 Tbsp flax seeds

1 cup milk, skim

1 cup cut spinach, raw

¼ cup dry oats, regular or quick

1 cup water

1 cup ice (optional)

INSTRUCTIONS:

Blend the milk and strawberries in a blender until smooth.

Add mango, chia seeds, flax seeds, spinach, oats, and water and blend until smooth.

Serve in a tall glass.

Icons:

Tropical Smoothie

INGREDIENTS:

2 cups raw baby spinach

2 cups coconut water

¾ cup fresh chunked pineapple

½ cup fresh mango

½ Tbsp chia seeds

1 Tbsp flax seeds, whole

1 cup ice (optional)

INSTRUCTIONS:

Blend spinach and coconut water in a blender until green, smooth and free from chunks of spinach.

Add the mango, pineapple, flax seeds, and chia seeds, blending until smooth and creamy.

Pour into glass and enjoy.

Icons: 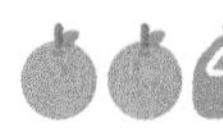 

Salmon Pasta with Asparagus

INGREDIENTS:

1 cup cooked (½ cup dry) whole wheat pasta

3 oz salmon, Arctic wild

2 tsp olive oil

Dash of salt and pepper

1 medium slice, ⅛-inch-thick, yellow onion

2 cups cut asparagus, cooked from fresh

INSTRUCTIONS:

Generously salt and pepper a 3-ounce piece of Arctic wild salmon that has been cleaned and scaled.

Cut a ⅛-inch-thick slice of medium yellow onion.

Chop two cups of asparagus.

Once these steps are done, turn on the oven to 425 degrees Fahrenheit.

Once a medium-sized sauté pan is hot, coat it with olive oil and place the salmon in the pan, skin side down. Once the salmon is in the pan, let it sear for about 5 minutes on one side, making the skin side crispy. Then, flip the salmon skin side up and place it in the oven for 15–25 minutes.

While the salmon is in the oven, fill a large pot halfway with salted water.

Once the water is boiling, place half a cup of whole wheat pasta inside the pot and allow to boil. Once the pasta is al dente (tender but provides some resistance when bitten), remove it from heat. Drain and cool the pasta with running water.

Heat a medium-sized sauté pan over medium-high heat. Once the sauté pan is heated, add a tablespoon of olive oil, along with the onion and asparagus. Allow the vegetables to cook thoroughly until they are tender and slightly golden brown on the edges.

Add a dash of salt and pepper to taste.

Remove salmon from the oven and set aside for 5 minutes.

Serve pasta topped with vegetables and salmon.

Icons: 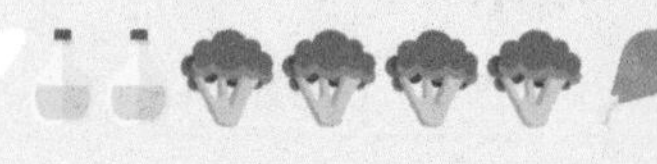

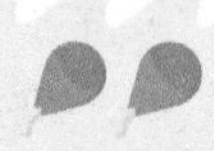

Baked Salmon with Soba Noodles and Vegetables

INGREDIENTS:

2 oz salmon, Arctic, wild

1 cup chopped broccoli, fresh or frozen

3 oz soba noodle, buckwheat-based

1 Tbsp chopped, garlic

1 Tbsp onion powder

Dash of Himalayan salt (or iodized salt) and pepper

1 cup diced squash, summer zucchini, including skin

½ cup chopped red bell peppers

Bragg's All-Purpose Seasoning, Liquid Aminos

INSTRUCTIONS:

Preheat oven to 425 degrees Fahrenheit.

Generously salt and pepper a 2-ounce piece of Arctic wild salmon that has been cleaned and scaled.

Chop ½ cup red bell pepper.

Dice 1 cup of summer squash zucchini.

Heat a medium-sized sauté pan and coat it with olive oil.

Place the salmon in the pan skin side down. Let it sear for about 5 minutes on one side, making the skin side crispy. Then flip the salmon skin side up and place it in the oven for 15–25 minutes.

Once the salmon is in the oven boil a large pot filled halfway with salted water. When the water is boiling, place half a cup of buckwheat soba noodles in and allow to boil. Once the pasta is al dente (tender but provides some resistance when bitten), remove it from heat. Drain and cool with running water.

Heat a medium-sized sauté pan over medium-high heat. Place a tablespoon of olive oil in the pan and add the red bell pepper and squash along with the onion powder and chopped garlic. Allow the vegetables to cook thoroughly until they are tender and slightly golden brown on the edges. Then add the liquid amino seasoning into the pan of the salmon and allow for that to cook down while pouring the liquid over the salmon.

Remove the salmon from the oven and let it stand for 5 minutes.

Serve pasta topped with vegetables and salmon.

Icons:      

Turkey Breast Dinner

INGREDIENTS:

3 oz turkey breast, oven-roasted, sliced

2 slices avocado, black skin, California type

1 cup spinach, raw

1 tsp garlic powder

2 tsp onion powder

INSTRUCTIONS:

Place spinach on a plate, then layer with turkey breast and season with garlic and onion powder.

Top with 2 slices avocado.

Icons: 

Mustard Crusted Albacore Tuna Steak

INGREDIENTS:

3 oz tuna, albacore

1 cup spinach, raw

1 cup squash or summer zucchini, skin on

1 tsp olive oil

1 Tbsp garlic powder

1 Tbsp onion powder

½ cup bread crumbs, panko

1 tsp crushed red pepper flakes

1 tsp ground black pepper

1 tsp Himalayan pink salt or iodized salt

1 Tbsp Dijon mustard

INSTRUCTIONS:

Preheat oven to 400 degrees Fahrenheit.

Season a 3-ounce piece of albacore tuna with salt and pepper. Then spread Dijon mustard evenly over all the surfaces of the tuna.

In a small bowl, combine breadcrumbs, garlic powder, onion powder, and red pepper flakes.

Roll the tuna in the breadcrumb mixture, creating an even coating.

Season sliced summer zucchini squash with salt and pepper.

Heat a medium-sized sauté skillet using medium-high heat.

Once heated, place ½ teaspoon of olive oil into the pan.

Place the coated tuna into the pan, skin side down. Sear and brown all sides of the tuna. Once the tuna has been seared, place it in the oven and cook for 15 to 20 minutes, until reaching an internal temperature of 140-145 degrees Fahrenheit.

In a medium-sized skillet on medium heat, add ½ teaspoon of olive oil, zucchini, and spinach and sauté for 5 minutes or until the vegetables are cooked through and golden brown.

Serve hot.

Icons:    

Fried Egg and Avocado Sandwich

INGREDIENTS:

2 slices whole wheat toast, plain

2 large whole eggs, fried

1 oz Monterey Jack or cheddar cheese, shredded

2 slices avocado, black skin, California type

1 dash pink Himalayan salt or iodized salt

2 dashes black pepper, ground

1 slice red tomato, raw

INSTRUCTIONS:

Make two fried eggs, cooking for 2 minutes until they no longer stick to the pan. (I suggest using a non-stick pan.) Season with salt and pepper. With a spatula, flip eggs and cook until the yolk and egg whites are cooked and there is no longer liquid.

Toast 2 slices of whole wheat bread in the toaster.

With a spatula, place the cooked eggs on the bottom slice of toast.

Top eggs with 2 tablespoons of shredded cheese; cover, and let cheese melt.

Serve sandwich with 2 slices of avocado and slice of tomato.

Icons: 

Chicken and Mushroom Pasta

INGREDIENTS:

3 oz chicken breast, skinless

2 tsp black pepper, ground

1 tsp pink Himalayan salt or iodized salt

½ cup cooked yellow onion, chopped

½ cup mushrooms, cooked from fresh

1 cup whole wheat pasta

½ cup tomato-based marinara sauce

INSTRUCTIONS:

Preheat oven to 400 degrees Fahrenheit.

Season chicken with salt and pepper.

Put olive oil in a large skillet and heat to medium-high heat.

Once the oil is heated, place the seasoned chicken breast in the pan.

Cook the chicken until all sides are golden brown.

Once the sides are brown, bake the chicken at 400 degrees Fahrenheit until the internal temperature is 165 degrees.

Once the chicken has reached 165 degrees, place it to the side for 5 to 10 minutes.

While the chicken is browning, dice yellow onion and mushrooms.

Fill a medium-size pot with salted water. Bring to a boil.

Add pasta to the water and cook until al dente.

Drain and rinse pasta. Let stand for 5 minutes.

Meanwhile, take a medium-sized sauté pan and heat it to medium-high heat with a tablespoon of oil. Mix the mushrooms with salt and pepper, having an even coating on all of them. Then, while cooking the mushrooms, add the onions and cook both until they are brown and caramelized.

In a medium-sized pot, combine marinara sauce and caramelized vegetables. Simmer for about 5 minutes. Then turn off the heat and remove.

Serve the pasta hot and topped with the mushroom sauce and chicken.

Icons: 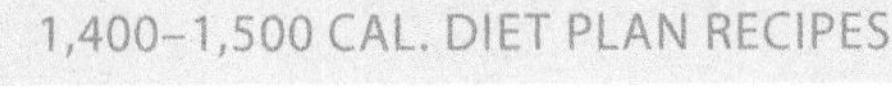

Oat Bowl

INGREDIENTS:

1 cup dry rolled oats or steel-cut oats

1 Tbsp almond butter

⅔ cup low-fat yogurt or Greek yogurt

¼ cup fresh blueberries

½ banana (sliced)

2 cups water

INSTRUCTIONS:

Make oats according to directions.

Let oats sit for 5 minutes or desired thickness.

Add yogurt, almond butter, and fruits.

Icons: 

Black Bean Taco Salad

INGREDIENTS:

2 cups shredded lettuce, fresh

3.5 oz ground turkey, lean, fat-free

Dash of salt and pepper, to taste

1 tsp garlic powder

½ cup yellow onion, diced

¼ cup corn

2 Tbsp tomato salsa

¼ cup black beans, canned, drained

2 Tbsp mashed avocado, black skin

INSTRUCTIONS:

In a medium-sized skillet over medium-high heat, add turkey and half of the chopped yellow onion.

Season with garlic powder and remove from heat when all of the turkey is brown and reaches an internal temperature of 165 degrees Fahrenheit.

In a small bowl, combine the remaining raw onion, yellow corn, tomato salsa, and drained black beans. Mix together and add salt, pepper, and garlic powder.

Once the vegetables are adequately mixed, shred lettuce and place on a large plate. Place the ground turkey and vegetable mix atop the lettuce. Add 2 Tbsp of avocado to the salad.

Icons: 

Ground Turkey and Brussels Sprout Salad

INGREDIENTS:

2 oz ground turkey, extra lean, fat-free

1 cup spinach raw

1 Tbsp garlic powder

⅓ cup chopped yellow onion

7 cherry tomatoes, chopped

½ cup Brussels sprouts, fresh

½ cup peas, green, frozen

½ tsp olive oil

1 tsp apple cider vinegar dressing

INSTRUCTIONS:

In a medium-sized skillet heat turkey, garlic, and onion with medium-high heat until brown and fragrant.

Boil 3 cups of water in a medium-sized pot and add the green frozen peas, boiling them until they are no longer frozen but firm and fork-tender, then drain the liquids from the peas.

In a medium-sized sauté pan that is set on medium-high heat, cook the Brussels sprouts until brown and golden.

Place 1 cup of raw spinach on a plate, adding the chopped cherry tomatoes and Brussels sprouts, then add the peas and cooked ground turkey to the salad. For salad dressing, take a mix of olive oil and apple cider vinegar and use this as a dressing.

Icons: 

Chicken Stir Fry over Rice

INGREDIENTS:

3 oz chicken breast, skinless, chopped

1 cup broccoli, fresh

½ cup peas, green, frozen

½ cup onions

½ cup watercress

⅔ cup brown rice

1 tsp garlic powder

Dash of salt and pepper

2 tsp Bragg's All-Purpose Seasoning, Liquid Aminos

1⅓ cup vegetable broth, bouillon, or consommé

INSTRUCTIONS:

Season chicken with salt and pepper and garlic powder.

Put olive oil in a large skillet and heat to medium-high heat.

Once the oil is hot, place the seasoned chicken breast into the pan. Cook the chicken until brown on all sides and until the inside of the breast is opaque with an internal temperature of 165 degrees Fahrenheit (using an instant-read thermometer).

Once the chicken has reached 165 degrees, set to the side for 5 to 10 minutes.

While the chicken is browning, in a medium pot combine brown rice and vegetable broth. Bring to a boil.

Once the rice is boiling, lower the temperature and simmer until there are gaps or holes visible between the rice grains, indicating the water has been absorbed.

Remove from heat and let stand for 5 minutes.

Once the rice is done, heat a large sauté pan using medium to high heat. Add 1 tablespoon of oil to the pan then add broccoli, peas, watercress, and onion.

Cook until vegetables are tender and golden around the edges. Once they are golden, add in the liquid aminos and cook until the vegetables are glossy.

Serve vegetables and chicken over rice.

Icons: 

Open-Face Chicken and Avocado Tortilla

INGREDIENTS:

8-inch whole wheat tortilla

½ cup red bell peppers, raw

½ cup spinach, fresh

2 Tbsp mashed avocado, black skin, California type

2 Tbsp hummus

3 oz chicken breast, skinless

½ tsp olive oil

½ tsp salt

1 tsp pepper

INSTRUCTIONS:

Preheat the oven to 400 degrees Fahrenheit.

Season skinless chicken breast with salt and pepper.

In a large skillet over medium-high heat, heat olive oil. Once the oil has heated, place the seasoned chicken breast into the pan, cooking the chicken until it is brown on all sides. Then place the chicken in the oven and continue cooking until the breast is opaque and has an internal temperature of 165 degrees Fahrenheit.

In a medium-sized sauté pan under medium heat, place the whole wheat tortilla, allowing it to get golden brown on one side. Flip and let the other side get golden as well.

Once both sides are golden brown, remove the tortilla from the pan and spread 2 tablespoons of hummus on the tortilla, adding the spinach and red peppers on top of the hummus.

Place the tortilla with the vegetables in the oven for 5 to 10 minutes, until the spinach withers and is dark green. Remove the tortilla from the oven and add the chicken and avocado.

Place the tortilla on a cutting board, cut into pieces, and serve.

Icons:

Chicken and Mushroom Pasta

INGREDIENTS:

1½ oz skinless chicken breast

1 cup whole wheat pasta

4 cups vegetable broth

¾ cup spinach, raw

½ cup yellow onion, chopped

1 tsp olive oil

¼ cup shredded carrots

¼ cup mushrooms, fresh

½ cup asparagus, fresh

1 tsp garlic powder

Dash of salt and pepper

INSTRUCTIONS:

Take a medium sauté pan and heat over medium-high heat. Season both sides of the chicken breast with a dash of salt, pepper, and garlic powder. Cook chicken until all sides are golden brown.

In a large pot, cook the pasta in boiling vegetable broth according to package directions. Drain and set aside.

Heat a medium-sized skillet over medium heat. Once heated, place oil in the pan then the spinach, carrots, mushrooms, asparagus, and onion and season with garlic powder. Stir the vegetables occasionally until they are all golden brown and tender. Remove from heat.

Mix the pasta, vegetables, and chicken together. Serve hot.

Icons:

Mustard Tuna Salad

INGREDIENTS:

1½ oz albacore tuna in water, no salt, drained

1 cup quinoa

2 cups vegetable broth

1 tsp salt and pepper

2 cups spinach, cut into pieces, raw

1¼ cups strawberries, raw

½ cup tangerine, sectioned, raw

2 walnut halves, chopped

2 pecan halves, chopped

Dijon mustard vinaigrette, homemade

- 2 Tbsp Dijon mustard
- 1 tsp olive oil
- Salt and pepper
- 1 Tbsp garlic powder
- 1 Tbsp oregano and thyme mixture
- 1 Tbsp lemon juice

INSTRUCTIONS:

Preheat oven to 400 degrees Fahrenheit.

Coat a medium-sized skillet pan with olive oil and heat over medium-high heat.

While the pan is heating up, season the tuna steak with salt and pepper evenly on all sides, then place the coated tuna into the pan, skin-side down. Sear and brown all sides of the tuna. Once the tuna has been seared, place it into the oven and cook for 15 to 20 minutes until it reaches an internal temperature of 140-145 degrees Fahrenheit.

In a medium pot, combine 1 cup quinoa and 2 cups vegetable broth and bring to a boil. Once boiling, lower the temperature and simmer until all the water is absorbed.

Remove from heat and set aside for 5 minutes.

In a large bowl, combine the spinach, sliced strawberries, sectioned tangerines, and chopped nuts.

Remove the tuna from the oven. After 2 minutes, cut lengthwise into ½-inch slices and place on top of the salad.

In a blender, place the ingredients for the Dijon vinaigrette and blend for about 2 minutes or until the liquid is uniform and consistent.

Icons: 

1,600–1,800 CAL. DIET PLAN RECIPES

Turkey Swiss Sandwich

INGREDIENTS:

2 slices whole wheat plain toast

2 oz rotisserie turkey, deli slices

1 medium slice ¼ inch thick red tomato

1 large leaf Bibb lettuce

1 oz red onion slice

½ slice Swiss cheese, ½ oz

1 Tbsp Dijon mustard

INSTRUCTIONS:

Between two slices of toasted whole wheat bread, layer Dijon mustard, 1 large leaf of bib lettuce, 1 slice of swiss cheese, 1 oz of sliced red onions, 1 medium slice of tomato, and 2 ounces of rotisserie turkey slices. Add yogurt, almond butter and fruits.

Icons:

Chicken Cilantro Quesadilla

INGREDIENTS:

Two, 6-inch-diameter whole wheat tortillas

1 oz (or 2 Tbsp) cheddar cheese, natural, 25% reduced fat, grated

¼ cup chopped red bell pepper

½ cup chopped yellow onion

¼ cup chopped red tomato

1 cup spinach

2 oz shredded chicken breast, cooked

½ cup shredded lettuce, fresh

2 Tbsp cilantro leaves

INSTRUCTIONS:

In a medium-sized sauté pan over medium-high heat, cook the onions, peppers, spinach, and tomatoes for 2-3 minutes until tender.

Once tender, remove from heat and set aside.

In a large, non-stick skillet over low-medium heat, place one tortilla and top with cheese, onions, peppers, tomatoes, spinach, and chicken.

Once the cheese is melted and the toppings are warm, add the lettuce and cilantro and top with the other tortilla.

Use a spatula to flip the quesadilla so both sides cook to golden-brown.

Once both sides are golden-brown, remove from heat, cut, and serve hot.

Icons:

Chicken Lettuce Wraps

INGREDIENTS:

Iceberg lettuce

1½ oz chicken breast, skinless, chopped

½ cup mushrooms, fresh

2 tsp Bragg's All-Purpose Seasoning, Liquid Aminos

½ cup shredded carrots

⅔ cup brown rice

1½ cups water

1 tsp onion powder

1 tsp garlic powder

1 small apple, fresh, chopped

6 chopped raw almonds

INSTRUCTIONS:

Over medium-high heat, coat a medium-sized skillet with olive oil.

Add the chopped chicken, garlic powder, and onion powder to the pan. Stir in seasonings and brown the chicken until its pink color is no longer visible. Add the mushrooms and cook with 2 teaspoons of liquid aminos. Cook for 2 more minutes, reducing the liquid. When done, remove from heat and let cool.

Boil brown rice in twice as much water; once boiling, reduce to a simmer. Remove the rice from heat once it has absorbed all the water.

To a small bowl, add shredded carrots, chopped apples, and almonds. Mix together.

Next, add the chicken and brown rice and mix gently together.

Once done, take a lettuce leaf and fill half with the chicken rice mixture, then tightly roll toward the unfilled side, making a wrap.

Icons: 

Grilled Chicken with Garlicked Vegetables

INGREDIENTS:

2 oz chicken breast, skinless

½ cup chopped broccoli, fresh

½ cup squash, summer, zucchini, including skin

¼ cup yellow onion, chopped

1 cup spinach

Dash of salt and black pepper

1 Tbsp garlic powder

INSTRUCTIONS:

Season chicken with salt, pepper, and garlic powder.

Put olive oil in a large skillet and heat over medium-high heat.

Once the oil is heated, place the seasoned chicken into the pan. Sear and cook all sides of the chicken breast until it is golden brown. Cook until the internal temperature is 165 degrees, or the chicken is leaking clear liquids if poked with a knife.

Once the chicken has reached the correct internal temperature, place to the side for 5 to 10 minutes.

In a medium skillet coated with olive oil, combine fresh chopped broccoli with sliced zucchini with the skin on, onion, and spinach. Cook until they are thoroughly heated or until slightly golden-brown around the edges and sides.

Add in the chopped garlic and cook for an additional 2 minutes, stirring the vegetables in the pan to incorporate the garlic flavors.

Slice the chicken breast into strips about 1 inch thick and serve hot over the hot vegetables.

Icons: 

Scrambled Eggs

INGREDIENTS:

1 medium egg

1 Tbsp water

Dash of pink Himalayan or iodized salt

Dash black pepper

2 oz spinach, raw

½ cup red bell pepper, raw, diced

INSTRUCTIONS:

Coat a medium-sized sauté pan with olive oil and heat to medium heat.

Add spinach and diced red pepper and cook for about 1-2 minutes, until softened.

In a bowl, mix the egg and water.

Add egg to the vegetables and season with salt and pepper. Scramble.

Serve hot.

Icons: 

Steamy Buttered Halibut with Red Potatoes and Asparagus

INGREDIENTS:

2 oz halibut

1 tsp garlic powder

2 tsp onion powder

1 tsp butter

1 Tbsp paprika

1 tsp thyme, dried

1 tsp cayenne pepper, ground

1 lemon, juiced, raw

1 cup asparagus, fresh

1 tsp olive oil

1 cup small red potatoes, baked

INSTRUCTIONS:

Preheat oven to 400 degrees Fahrenheit.

Seal red potatoes inside a medium sheet of aluminum foil and bake in the oven for 45 to 55 minutes, until they are fork tender.

Combine garlic powder, onion powder, paprika, thyme, and cayenne pepper in a small bowl and coat halibut with the seasoning mixture.

Once seasoned, place the fish and lemon juice inside a pocket made from foil. Seal the foil edges tightly.

Place into a 400 degree Fahrenheit oven for 25 to 30 minutes until the fish is cooked to an internal temperature of 145 degrees Fahrenheit. After cooking, remove from the oven, top with butter, and set aside for 5 minutes.

In a small sauté pan coated with olive oil, over medium-high heat, place asparagus, seasoned with salt and pepper.

Cook asparagus until tender, turning the vegetables periodically.

Once the fish, vegetables, and potatoes are all done, place the asparagus on a plate, along with the potatoes and halibut. If desired, squeeze additional lemon juice on the fish and vegetables.

Icons:

Orange Shredded Chicken

INGREDIENTS:

2 oz chicken breast, shredded

2 fluid oz orange juice, fresh

1 Tbsp onion powder

1 Tbsp garlic powder

1 Tbsp cornstarch

1½ cups of bok choy, cut in pieces

3 tsp Bragg's All-Purpose Seasoning, Liquid Aminos

1 cup brown rice

2 cups water

1 oz water

INSTRUCTIONS:

Boil or broil chicken until internal temperature reaches 165 degrees Fahrenheit. Cool. Shred.

Place 2 cups water and 1 cup brown rice in a medium-sized pot and bring to a boil. Once boiling, reduce the heat to low and cover, letting the rice absorb the liquid.

In a medium pot, combine orange juice, ½ tablespoon of garlic powder and 1 teaspoon Bragg's Liquid Aminos. Bring to a boil.

Once boiling, turn the sauce on low for about 15-20 minutes or until the liquid has reduced by half. Once the liquid has reduced, mix the cornstarch with 1 ounce of water in a cup until there are no clumps. Slowly combine the cornstarch mixture with the orange juice sauce and stir slowly until it thickens. Once the sauce is thick and smooth, remove the pot from the heat.

Chop bok choy into small pieces

Coat a medium sauté pan with olive oil and heat over medium-high heat. Once the pan is hot, place the bok choy pieces into the pan along with the rest of the garlic powder and liquid aminos and cook until the vegetables are tender.

Place the shredded chicken in the pan with the bok choy and pour the orange glaze over the top of the vegetables and the chicken and mix together.

Once the glaze is absorbed, take the lid off and serve.

Serve in a bowl or a plate with rice topped with chicken and vegetable mixture.

Icons: 

Buttered Salmon with Brussels Sprouts

INGREDIENTS:

1 cup Brussels sprouts, fresh

1 Tbsp parsley

2 oz salmon, Arctic, wild

1 cup brown rice

2 cups water

¼ cup yellow onion, chopped

1 tsp butter, unsalted

1 Tbsp water

INSTRUCTIONS:

In a medium pot, combine brown rice and parsley with water and cook per instructions. Once the liquid has absorbed, remove the rice from heat and set aside.

Halve the Brussels sprouts and put them face down in a medium-sized skillet over medium-high heat.

Add onions.

Cook until both the Brussels sprouts and onion turn light golden-brown.

Over medium-high heat, place the salmon skin-side down in a small sauté pan.

Cook the salmon until it's golden brown on all sides, flipping occasionally. Once golden on all sides, place the butter and water into the pan. Use a spoon to pour the hot, buttery liquid over the salmon.

Serve layered with vegetables and salmon over rice.

Icons: 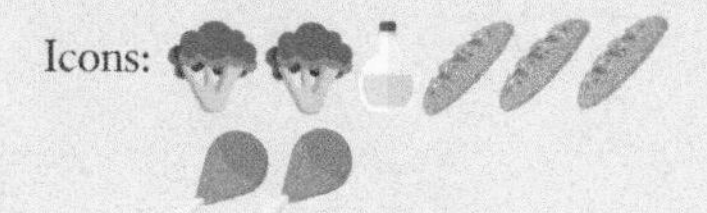

Turkey Macaroni and Cheese with Asparagus

INGREDIENTS:

2 oz ground turkey, lean (7% fat, 93% lean meat)

1 cup macaroni noodles, whole wheat

2 cups water

1 oz cheddar cheese, shredded

1 Tbsp chili powder

1 oz yellow onion

3 tsp garlic powder

1 cup asparagus, chopped, fresh

½ cup skim milk

½ tsp dry mustard

INSTRUCTIONS:

Put olive oil in a large skillet and heat over medium-high heat.

Mix the ground turkey in the skillet, along with the chili, garlic powder, and yellow onion. Cook until it is brown, evenly seasoned, and cooked thoroughly.

In another sauté pan coated with oil, over medium-high heat, add asparagus and cook for 5 minutes, or until the asparagus is tender and golden-brown around the edges

In a pot, combine 2 cups of water, a dash of salt, and 1 cup of whole wheat macaroni noodles. Cook on high until al dente.

Drain the water from the pasta.

After the pasta is drained, place it back in the pot and add the shredded cheese to the macaroni, along with the ½ cup of 2% milk and dry mustard. Cook on medium-high heat, stirring frequently until the cheese is melted and covers the noodles evenly.

Once the cheese is melted, add the turkey and vegetables.

Lower the heat to low and stir them together, mixing thoroughly and evenly for about 5 minutes, or until the liquid is reduced.

Serve hot.

Icons: 

Ham English Muffin

INGREDIENTS:

1 whole wheat English muffin

2 oz deli meat, ham, sliced

1 slice cheddar cheese

2 cups spinach, fresh

½ cup red bell peppers

½ cup yellow onion, chopped

1 tsp black pepper, ground

Dash of pink Himalayan salt or iodized salt

INSTRUCTIONS:

Over medium-high heat, cook spinach, red peppers, yellow onion, salt, and black pepper in a medium-sized sauté pan coated with olive oil for 5 minutes, or until tender and/or golden-brown.

Once the vegetables are done, remove from heat, top with cheese, and cover with a lid until cheese melts.

Place deli sliced ham in a small pan over medium-high heat until ham is warm or hot throughout.

Toast the 2 halves of an English muffin until slightly golden-brown.

Between the muffin, sandwich layers of ham and cheesy vegetables.

Serve hot.

Icons:

Chicken Hemp Salad

INGREDIENTS:

2 oz chicken breast, skinless

2 cups mixed greens, lettuce

2 Tbsp low-calorie dressing

1 cup cucumber, raw with peel

½ cup cherry tomatoes, raw

½ cup garbanzo/chickpeas, canned, drained, cooked

½ cup croutons, store-bought

½ cup shredded carrots

1 tsp hemp seeds, hulled

1 tsp garlic powder

1 tsp onion powder

1 tsp salt and black pepper (ground)

INSTRUCTIONS:

Preheat oven to 400 degrees Fahrenheit.

Season chicken with salt, pepper, garlic powder, and onion powder.

Put olive oil in a large skillet and heat over medium-high heat.

Once the oil is heated, place the seasoned chicken into the pan.

Sear and cook all sides of the chicken breast until it is golden-brown. After all sides are brown, put the chicken breast into the oven and cook until the internal temperature is 165 degrees, or the chicken is leaking clear liquids if poked with a knife.

Remove the chicken from the oven once done and cut it lengthwise, getting as many slices as possible from the breast.

In a bowl, combine mixed greens, garbanzos, cucumbers, tomatoes, carrots, croutons, hemp seeds, and Italian dressing. Serve on a plate with sliced chicken on top.

Icons: 

Lime Beef Tenderloin and Avocado Salad

INGREDIENTS:

2 oz beef loin, broiled/grilled

¼ cup black beans, canned, drained

½ Tbsp salt

½ Tbsp black pepper

½ Tbsp white pepper

1 medium sweet potato, baked

2 cups spinach, raw

½ cup tomato, red, raw, chopped

½ cup red bell pepper, chopped

¼ cup canned chickpeas

2 slices avocado

2 Tbsp lime juice, fresh

INSTRUCTIONS:

Preheat oven to 450 degrees.

Heat a heavy 12-inch skillet over medium-high heat.

Season the beef generously with salt, black pepper, and white pepper.

Sear the beef in the skillet on all 4 sides until browned, about 3 to 4 minutes per side.

Transfer into a roasting pan.

Roast until desired done-ness is reached (120-125 degrees internal temperature for medium-rare, about 30 minutes). Set the meat aside, covered loosely with aluminum foil, for 10 minutes before serving.

Slice the beef into ½-inch to ¾-inch slices when ready to serve.

While the meat is cooking, with a knife poke holes in the sweet potato around all the surfaces. Wrap in aluminum foil. Place the potato in the oven for about 35 to 40 minutes, until the potato is tender.

In a large bowl, combine spinach, chopped bell peppers, chickpeas, tomato, and black beans.

On a large plate with the potato as a side, serve the salad with the beef loin on top. Pour lime juice on top of the salad to finish as a dressing.

Serve hot and garnish with avocado slices.

Icons:

Spaghetti Squash and Chicken Pasta with Basil Pesto

INGREDIENTS:

2 cups spaghetti squash

1 tsp Himalayan pink salt

½ tsp black pepper

2 oz chicken breast, skinless, chopped into cubes

1 Tbsp garlic powder

1 Tbsp onion powder

2 cups basil, fresh

2 cloves garlic

½ tsp olive oil

1-2 Tbsp water

INSTRUCTIONS:

Preheat the oven to 400°F.

Slice the spaghetti squash in half lengthwise and scoop out the seeds and ribbing.

Sprinkle squash with salt and pepper.

Poke holes in the spaghetti squash with a fork, then place cut-side down on a baking sheet.

Roast for 30 to 40 minutes, or until lightly browned on the outside, fork tender, but still a little firm. The time will vary depending on the size of your squash.

Remove from the oven and flip the squash so that its cut side is up. When cool to the touch, use a fork to scrape and fluff the strands from the inside of the squash.

Place squash strands in a bowl.

Over medium-high heat, in a medium non-stick skillet pan, place 2 ounces of chicken breast cubes seasoned with garlic and onion powder.

Sear and cook each side of the cubes until they are golden-brown with an internal temperature of 165 degrees Fahrenheit. Remove from heat when done.

Blend basil, garlic, and olive oil in a blender. Then add a couple of tablespoons of water and blend until smooth and sauce-like.

Mix spaghetti squash, chicken cubes, and the basil pesto sauce together while still hot, making sure everything is evenly coated with the pesto and has a bright green and orange color.

Serve hot.

Icons:

Smoked Salmon with Vegetables

INGREDIENTS:

2½ oz smoked salmon

1 cup summer squash or zucchini, includes skin

1 cup chopped asparagus, fresh

1 cup brown rice, steamed

1 tsp olive oil

1 Tbsp onion powder

1 Tbsp garlic powder

2 tsp thyme, dried

3 dashes black pepper, ground

1 Tbsp water

1 tsp butter

INSTRUCTIONS:

Cook rice per package instructions. Once the liquid has absorbed, remove the rice from heat and set aside with lid on.

Under medium heat, in a medium-sized skillet combine oil, chopped asparagus and zucchini. Season vegetables with onion powder, garlic powder, pepper, and thyme.

Stir vegetables occasionally until they are golden-brown and tender. Remove from heat.

In a small sauté pan over medium-high heat, place the salmon skin-side down and cook until golden-brown on all sides. Once golden on all sides, put butter and water in the pan. With a spoon, pour the hot butter over the salmon. Once done, remove from heat.

Serve rice topped with salmon and vegetables.

Icons:

Steamed Halibut with Red Potatoes and Asparagus

INGREDIENTS:

2 oz halibut

1 tsp garlic powder

2 tsp onion powder

1 Tbsp paprika

1 tsp thyme, dried

1 tsp cayenne pepper, ground

1 lemon, juiced, fresh

1 tsp butter

1 cup asparagus, fresh

1 tsp olive oil

½ tsp salt

½ tsp black pepper

1 cup small red potatoes, red skin

INSTRUCTIONS:

Preheat oven to 400 degrees Fahrenheit.

Seal red potatoes inside a medium sheet of aluminum foil and bake in the oven for 45 to 55 minutes, until they are fork tender.

Combine garlic powder, onion powder, paprika, and cayenne pepper. Coat halibut with seasoning mixture.

Once seasoned, place the fish inside a pocket made from foil. Seal the foil edges tightly.

Once wrapped, bake for 25 to 30 minutes, until it is cooked to an internal temperature of 145 degrees Fahrenheit. After cooking, remove from the oven and set aside for 5 minutes.

In a small sauté pan coated with olive oil, over medium-high heat, place asparagus, seasoned with salt and pepper.

Cook asparagus until tender, turning the vegetables periodically.

Once the fish, vegetables, and potatoes are all done, place the asparagus on a plate, along with the potatoes. Top the halibut with butter. Finish by adding a squeeze of lemon juice to the fish and vegetables.

Icons: 

Black Bean Quesadilla

INGREDIENTS:

½ cup black beans, canned, drained

½ oz cheddar cheese, 25% reduced fat

½ cup green bell pepper, raw

½ cup red bell pepper, raw

½ cup yellow onion, chopped

½ cup tomato, raw, chopped

1 cup spinach, fresh

Two 6" tortillas, whole wheat

INSTRUCTIONS:

Over medium-high heat, in a medium-sized sauté pan, combine onions, peppers, spinach, and tomatoes. Cook for 2-3 minutes, or until tender. Once done, take the vegetables off the heat and place to the side.

In a large skillet, over low-medium heat, place one of the tortillas. Top it with cheese, onions, peppers, tomatoes, spinach, and beans.

Once the cheese is melted and the toppings are warm, add the other tortilla on top, with the vegetables sandwiched between the two tortillas. Use a spatula to flip and press down on the quesadilla to mash the beans. Cook until both sides are golden brown.

Once both sides are golden-brown, remove the tortilla, cut and serve hot.

Icons: 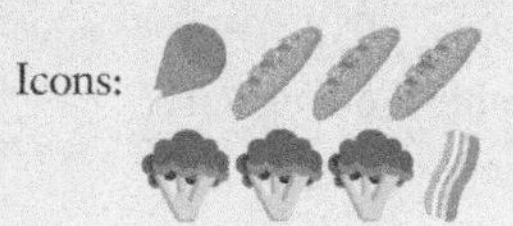

Chicken Marsala

INGREDIENTS:

2½ oz. chicken breast, skin on

½ cup brown button mushrooms, sliced

1 Tbsp Marsala cooking wine

½ cup yellow onion, diced

1 tsp butter, unsalted

1 tsp oregano, dried

1 cup angel hair pasta, whole wheat

1 Tbsp heavy cream

½ cup vegetable broth

2 Tbsp garlic, fresh, chopped

¼ cup all-purpose flour

2 Tbsp Parmesan cheese, dry

INSTRUCTIONS:

Boil a large pot of water for the pasta. Cook according to the package directions, until al dente.

Cut the chicken breast into bite-sized pieces, sprinkle with oregano, and then coat in the flour.

Add butter to a skillet over medium heat.

Once the skillet is hot, add the coated chicken and cook it for 5-6 minutes. Stir the chicken occasionally, until slightly browned. Take the chicken out of the pan and set aside.

In the skillet, add mushrooms, garlic, and onions and cook for 5 minutes or until they have started to brown. Remove from pan.

Add the vegetable broth and marsala wine and cook for 2–3 minutes, until it bubbles.

Add the heavy cream, chicken, mushrooms, and onions to the pan and reduce the heat to medium, allowing the mixture to cook for a few minutes until the sauce has become thick and the chicken has cooked through with no pink in the middle.

Drain the pasta and toss it in with the sauce. Serve with shredded Parmesan cheese on top or mixed into the pasta.

Icons: 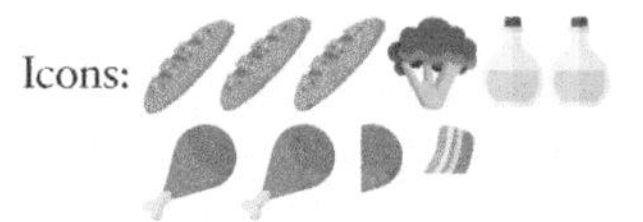

Arborio Risotto Rice with Parmesan Cheese

INGREDIENTS:

1 cup arborio risotto rice

1 cup asparagus, fresh

1 oz white wine

½ cup green peas, frozen

1 Tbsp lemon juice

2 Tbsp Parmesan cheese, dry, grated

2 tsp garlic powder

2 Tbsp yellow onion

3 tsp olive oil

¼ tsp pepper

⅛ tsp salt

4 cups vegetable broth or water

INSTRUCTIONS:

Cook rice per instructions.

Cut asparagus into 1-inch pieces; set aside.

Heat the vegetable broth in a saucepan over medium heat; simmer while preparing risotto.

Heat 3 tsp olive oil in a large skillet over medium heat. Cook and stir the onion, asparagus, and peas until they are tender, about 5 minutes. Stir in garlic powder, salt, pepper, and arborio rice; cook and stir until rice is lightly toasted, about 5 more minutes.

Pour white wine into rice mixture, stirring constantly, until liquid is evaporated, about 5 minutes. Stir broth into rice, one ladleful at a time, allowing liquid to absorb completely before adding more while stirring constantly, about 20 minutes. If rice is not soft and fluffy, continue to add broth until it is at the desired consistency. Add asparagus and stir.

Remove from heat and mix in Parmesan cheese, and lemon juice. Serve immediately.

Icons: 

Quick Shrimp and Parmesan Pasta

INGREDIENTS:

6 shrimp, cooked from frozen

1 Tbsp lemon juice

2 Tbsp Parmesan cheese grated, dry

1⅓ cups whole wheat pasta

3 tsp olive oil

2 Tbsp parsley

INSTRUCTIONS:

In a large pot cook the pasta in boiling water according to package directions. Drain and set aside.

In the same pot, add 1 tsp olive oil. Add the shrimp and cook until the shrimp start to turn pink.

Add the pasta back to the pot with the remaining oil, parmesan, and parsley.

Add the lemon juice before serving and serve while hot.

Icons:

Egg White Western Omelet

INGREDIENTS:

2 egg whites

2 Tbsp skim milk

½ oz ham, cubed, 95% fat-free

¼ cup red bell peppers, raw

¼ cup mushrooms, fresh

¼ cup yellow onion, chopped

1 tsp garlic powder

1 Tbsp jalapeño peppers, fresh

1 tsp pink Himalayan or iodized salt

INSTRUCTIONS:

Spray an 8-inch nonstick sauté or omelet pan with cooking spray and heat over medium heat.

Add the ham, bell peppers, jalapeño pepper, mushrooms, garlic powder, and onion; cook 4 minutes or until vegetables are just tender, and the ham is golden-brown around the edges. Stir occasionally.

When tender, place the mix into a small bowl, sprinkle with salt, and cover to keep warm.

Carefully wipe out pan with paper towels; spray pan again with cooking spray.

In a small bowl, mix the egg whites and milk together until blended.

Pour the eggs into the pan over medium heat. Loosely cover the pan with aluminum foil and cook 1½ minutes, or until edges start to set.

Using a rubber spatula, gently lift edges while tilting pan to allow uncooked whites to run beneath. Cook just until set.

Place the ham and vegetables over half of the cooked whites. Fold over the other half to cover vegetables.

Serve hot.

Icons:

Chicken and Mushroom Pasta

INGREDIENTS:

1½ oz chicken breast, skinless

1 cup whole wheat pasta

4 cups vegetable broth

¾ cup spinach, raw

½ cup yellow onion, chopped

1 tsp olive oil

½ cup shredded carrots

½ cup mushrooms, fresh

½ cup asparagus, cut into pieces

1 tsp garlic powder

Dash of salt and pepper

INSTRUCTIONS:

In a large pot, cook the pasta in boiling vegetable broth according to package directions. Drain and set aside.

In a medium-sized skillet over medium heat mix the oil, spinach, carrots, mushrooms, asparagus, onion, and garlic powder. Stir the vegetables occasionally, until they are golden-brown and tender. Remove from heat once tender.

Take a medium sauté pan with oil and heat over medium-high heat. Season the chicken breast with a dash of salt, pepper, and garlic powder on both sides of the chicken breast. Then place the chicken into the pan, letting it cook until all sides are golden-brown.

Mix the pasta, vegetables, and chicken together. Serve while hot.

Icons:

Herb and Cheese Red Potato Hash

INGREDIENTS:

2 cups chopped spinach

2 Tbsp water

1 cup red potatoes

1 tsp olive oil

1 tsp rosemary, dried

1 Tbsp thyme, dried

3 Tbsp shredded cheddar cheese

1 tsp sea salt

INSTRUCTIONS:

In a medium bowl, toss the potatoes with olive oil, the dried rosemary and thyme, and sea salt.

In a skillet over medium heat, add the potatoes and cook until just tender, about 12-15 minutes. Removed the potatoes from the skillet (leaving any liquid) and set them aside in a separate bowl.

In the same skillet, cook the spinach with 2 Tbsp of water about 5 minutes.

When the spinach is tender, add the potatoes and the cheese. Stir to combine everything and let cook for another 3 minutes to melt the cheese.

Remove and serve hot.

Icons:

Maple-Glazed Salmon Pomegranate Salad

INGREDIENTS:

2 oz smoked salmon

1½ Tbsp maple syrup

2 tsp apple cider vinegar

2 tsp butter, unsalted

1 cup quinoa

2 cups water

2 cups spinach, raw, cut into pieces

2 walnut halves

½ cup shredded carrots

1 Tbsp cranberries, dried, sweetened, whole pieces

¼ cup clementine, raw, segmented

½ cup whole pieces of Brussels sprouts, fresh, halved

½ cup yellow onion

⅓ cup pomegranate seeds (about ¼ of a whole pomegranate)

2 Tbsp Dijon mustard vinaigrette

½ cup sweet corn, whole kernel

¼ cup tomato, red, raw, chopped

¼ cup red bell peppers, chopped

INSTRUCTIONS:

Preheat oven to 400 degrees Fahrenheit.

In a medium-sized pot, pour in 2 cups of water and 1 cup of quinoa, and bring to a boil. Once boiling, turn the heat to a simmer, cover, and let the quinoa absorb the water. When all water is absorbed, remove from heat and let cool.

Heat a medium-sized skillet pan coated in ½ tsp butter to medium-high heat.

When the pan is hot, place the salmon in the pan skin-side down, searing the salmon until it is golden-brown.

Flip the salmon bottom side-up, top it with ½ tsp of butter, and put it in the oven. Cook for 25 minutes until it is pink and opaque in the middle, with an internal temperature of 145 degrees Fahrenheit.

While the salmon is in the oven, in another medium-sized skillet coated with ½ tsp butter, heat the pan up to medium-high heat and place the halved Brussels sprouts into the pan face down. Sear the sprouts until the side that is face down is golden-brown, then flip.

Remove the salmon from the oven and in the original skillet add the maple syrup and butter, allowing them to heat up and bubble. As it reduces, it will create a sauce. Once the sauce has become glossy, spoon the liquid over the top of the salmon, creating a glaze, and set aside for 5 minutes.

Add the onions, corn, and red peppers to the sprouts and cook them until they are tender, about 5 to 8 minutes. Once done, remove from heat and let cool.

In a large bowl, mix together the spinach, quinoa, tomato, walnuts, cranberries, pomegranate seeds, tangerine segments, carrots, apple cider vinegar, and Dijon mustard vinaigrette.

Serve salad mix on a plate, adding Brussels sprouts and topping with the maple-glazed salmon, creating a full savory and sweet meal. Enjoy!

Icons:

Salmon and Marinara Orzo Dinner

INGREDIENTS:

2 oz pan-seared salmon

⅔ cup orzo, whole wheat

½ cup peas, green, frozen

1 cup collard greens

3 Tbsp water

1 cup marinara sauce

INSTRUCTIONS:

In a small pot, combine orzo and water per directions. Once fluffy and all water is absorbed, remove from heat.

Place vegetables in a medium-sized pan with 2 Tbsp of water and cook for 5 minutes until tender. Remove from heat.

Heat a small sauté pan to medium-high heat. Once the pan is hot, place the salmon into the pan skin-side down and cook until it is golden-brown on all sides, flipping the salmon to different sides occasionally. Once golden on all sides, pour the marinara sauce into the pan, adding 1 Tbsp of water to the pan. Pour over and coat the salmon with the marinara sauce and let cook for 1-2 minutes, until the fish is coated and the sauce is hot. Remove from heat.

Serve orzo topped with vegetables and salmon.

Icons:

Chicken and Vegetable Lunch

INGREDIENTS:

2½ oz chicken breast

1 cup broccoli, fresh

½ cup peas, frozen

¼ cup red bell peppers

2 tsp Bragg's All-Purpose Seasoning, Liquid Aminos

1 tsp garlic powder

Dash salt and pepper

1 cup vegetable broth

INSTRUCTIONS:

After seasoning the chicken breast with a dash of salt, pepper, and the garlic powder on both sides, in a medium sauté pan under medium-high heat, cook the chicken until all sides are golden-brown and the internal temperature reaches 165 degrees Fahrenheit.

Chop all the vegetables.

Over medium heat, in a different pan, combine the chopped vegetables and broth. Cover with a lid and steam the vegetables until they are tender.

Once tender, add vegetables to the chicken and add the liquid aminos.

Serve hot.

Icons:

Savory Turkey and Brussels Sprout Salad

INGREDIENTS:

2 cups mixed greens, lettuce, chopped

3 oz turkey, white meat,
rotisserie deli cut

¼ cup tomato, cherry

¼ cup yellow onion, chopped

1 tsp olive oil

1 cup Brussels sprouts, fresh

½ cup peas, frozen

2 Tbsp low-calorie, low-fat dressing

½ cup corn, yellow, canned, drained

INSTRUCTIONS:

Slice Brussels sprouts in half.

In a medium-sized skillet over medium-high heat, add 1 tsp olive oil.

Sear the Brussels sprouts until golden-brown.

Cook on one side for 5 minutes. Flip and cook on the other side until golden-brown.

Then add remining vegetables excluding the salad greens into the pan and cook for 10 minutes, occasionally stirring, until they are all tender.

Line a large plate with the mixed greens.

Remove the vegetables from the pan and place on top of the greens. Cut the rotisserie deli turkey and place on top of the vegetables.

Top with dressing.

Icons:

Cinnamon Berry Oatmeal Bowl

INGREDIENTS:

1 cup oatmeal, regular

2 cups water

1 tsp cinnamon, ground

⅓ cup blueberries, raw

½ cup strawberries, raw

2 Tbsp slivered almonds, raw

1 Tbsp honey

INSTRUCTIONS:

Make oatmeal per package directions.

Once water comes to a boil, lower the heat and simmer until thickened, about 5 minutes.

When serving, add blueberries, strawberries, slivered raw almonds, honey, and cinnamon.

Stir and serve while hot.

Icons:

Fruity Summer Yogurt Bowl

INGREDIENTS:

¼ cup low-fat granola cereal

⅔ cup low-fat plain yogurt

¾ cup blueberries

1¼ cups sliced strawberries

INSTRUCTIONS:

Place yogurt in a bowl.

Pour cereal into yogurt bowl and mix.

Top with blueberries and strawberries.

Icons: 

Brussels Sprout and Quinoa Salad

INGREDIENTS:

1 cup Brussels sprouts, fresh, sliced in half

1 Tbsp olive oil

½ tsp salt and pepper

½ cup roasted corn

⅓ cup quinoa

½ cup tomato, red, raw, chopped

2 cups raw spinach

½ cup edamame beans, shelled and cooked

2 Tbsp reduced-calorie Italian dressing (optional)

INSTRUCTIONS:

In a large non-stick skillet over medium-high heat, add 1 tablespoon of olive oil and place the Brussels sprouts face down in the pan.

Season with salt and pepper.

Sear the sprouts for 2 minutes or more on one side until they are brown and golden. Then flip the sprouts and complete the same step, making the other side golden-brown.

Add in the corn and cook together until both are golden-brown.

Fill a pot with 2 cups of water and add quinoa.

Bring this to a boil. Once boiling, turn down the temperature to bring the water to a simmer and cover. Once the water is absorbed, remove the pot from the heat and let cool.

Combine the tender, golden-brown Brussels sprouts and corn with the raw spinach. Serve with the quinoa, chopped red tomatoes, and edamame beans.

Mix olive oil and apple cider vinegar and use this as a dressing or use a store-bought Italian dressing.

Icons:

Tips for Success

Food Records – Bring attention and focus to what is being consumed

Keep a record of everything consumed to improve the chances of success.

Keep track of daily activity.

Writing things down helps identify trends, pitfalls, emotions, and successes.

Beverages – They can add empty calories

Humans can't store water, so it needs to be consumed daily. Obviously, the amount needed varies from person to person, based on body size, age, gender, environmental conditions, individual sweat rate, and physical activity frequency and intensity. The Institute of Medicine recommends that women drink 9 cups of water, while men should drink 13 cups daily.

Many commonly consumed beverages contain lots of calories. For example, a cup of sweet tea has nearly 100 calories, while a 16-oz Starbucks Caramel Macchiato made with whole milk has 270 calories. While many beverages taste good, they are often empty calories, meaning they provide no nutritional benefit. They provide nothing but calories, usually in the form of fat and sugar.

Alcohol is calorie-dense. It provides 7 calories per gram and has the potential to be quite fattening when combined with high-fat foods like wings or French fries. Alcohol doesn't have to be completely eliminated, but be aware that it can slow down weight loss if not properly planned. Consuming alcohol should be carefully prearranged to accompany nutrient-dense, low-calorie meals.

Water, on the other hand, quenches thirst, satisfies the need for liquid, and has no calories. Thus, water is recommended. If possible, minimize or eliminate drinks like sodas and fancy coffees. Instead, add flavor to water by adding lemon or lime slices, and make teas and coffee without sugar. Skim milk is also a great alternative, as it provides calcium, vitamin D, protein, and other nutrients.

RECAP:

1. Drink water regularly.
2. Incorporate skim milk as needed to meet nutrient needs.
3. Minimize and pre-plan alcohol consumption.
4. Avoid drinks that only provide empty calories.

Eating Out – Don't let it be a pitfall

- Prepare in advance by packing fruit, sliced vegetables, low-fat string cheese, or unsalted nuts to eat during road trips.
- Choose water, low-fat milk, or other drinks without added sugars over soda or sweet tea.
- Start meals with a salad packed with vegetables and the dressing on the side.
- Divide and share an entree with others.
- Instead of an entree, order a side dish or an appetizer.
- Fill your plate with vegetables and fruit.
- Choose stir-fries, kabobs, or vegetarian menu items to fill your plate with vegetables.
- Select fruits for dessert.
- Check the menu for items that are low in calories and fat.
- Don't go to buffets.
- Choose steamed, grilled, or broiled dishes over those fried in oil or cooked in butter.
- Request 100% whole-wheat breads, rolls, and pasta.
- Don't clean your plate. Instead, leave half for another meal.
- Avoid salads made with mayonnaise (tuna, chicken, potato, macaroni, coleslaw).
- Order sandwiches with mustard instead of mayonnaise, tartar sauce, or special sauces.
- Remove the skin from poultry.
- Leave off the butter, gravy, and sauces.
- Choose a baked potato instead of French fries.
- If you must have sour cream, use low-fat.
- Top pizza with vegetables, rather than high-fat meats like sausage or pepperoni.
- Side dishes should be vegetables or a salad.

Grocery Store – Be the gatekeeper of what comes into your home environment

- Make a list from planned meals for the entire week before shopping.
- Choose the low-fat options for milk, cheese, yogurt, dressings, and gravies.
- Buy leaner cuts of meat to reduce fat.
- Limit buying salami, ham, corned beef, and bacon.
- Purchase fresh or frozen vegetables instead of canned.
- Check expiration and "best used by" dates.
- Use ice packs to keep cold products like meat and dairy cold when transporting them.
- Buy healthy staples like beans, pasta, and legumes in bulk when possible.
- To avoid impulse and unhealthy purchases, do not go to the grocery store when hungry.
- Budget for healthier foods.
- When planning your meals for the week, be intentional to include all the food groups.
- Shop the perimeter of the store, where the healthiest options are often found.
- Choose real, whole foods over processed packaged foods.
- When possible, avoid foods with added sugar.
- Look for and purchase foods with few ingredients.
- Avoid the aisles that contain pre-prepared frozen meals.

Quick Meal Tips – Planning ahead can keep you on track

- Pasta is fast and easy.
- Rice is easy to cook and can form the basis of any meal with meat.
- Salads can be bought already prepared (just monitor the amount of dressing).
- Chicken breasts can be quickly grilled.
- Cook in large amounts and freeze leftovers for a quick re-heat.
- Prep dinner in the morning.
- Use a slow cooker.
- Collect recipes.

• Intentionally plan leftovers.

• Keep a running grocery store list as items come up.

• Choose deveined shrimp over shrimp that have to be cleaned

• Use canned foods when appropriate, such as beans, tomatoes, and stocks.

• Regularly stock meal basics like pastas, rice, broths, stocks, canned tomatoes, extra virgin olive oil, and canned beans.

• Prepare menu items according to the time it takes to cook them. Start longer-cooking foods first, so that while it is cooking, other items can be prepared.

• Get children involved in making dinner.

• Supplement the main dish with prepared salads and/or side dishes.

Traveling Ideas – Being prepared is key

• Planning ahead is key.

• Pack perishable foods like fresh fruit, hard-boiled eggs, cut vegetables, cheese sticks in a cooler.

• Pack foods in small, resealable plastic storage bags in single-serving sizes.

• Drink plenty of water.

• Don't skip breakfast.

• Don't overeat by trying to eat three full restaurant meals each day you are away.

• Avoid or minimize alcohol.

• Eat protein with every meal to help curb hunger.

• Pack small liquid-y snacks like yogurt and applesauce under 3.4 oz (or pack your own); these are small and pose no threat to airport security.

• Pack dried fruit.

• Bring a snack bag of homemade energy bites, nuts, or trail mix.

• Carry a refillable water bottle in your travel bag.

• Buy lunch or dinner before boarding a plane. Options in the terminal will most likely be healthier and more customizable than the ones on the plane.

• Bring individual yogurt packs.

• Pack hummus and celery or baby carrots (keep sanitizing wipes with you).

• Pack rice cakes with almond or peanut butter.

- Stock the hotel refrigerator with healthy snacks to get through late-night munchies.
- If possible, stay at an Air BnB or a hotel that provides a kitchen or kitchenette if you don't mind cooking while you're traveling.

Snacking Ideas and Tips – Make nutrient-dense choices

- Mozzarella cheese sticks
- Cup of yogurt
- Red or green bell peppers with hummus or guacamole
- Greek yogurt mixed with berries
- Peanut butter on apple slices
- Unsalted nuts and seeds can be filling and nutrient-dense.
- Oatmeal squares or Cheerios in a zip-lock bag
- Fresh fruit is an ideal pre-portioned snack.
- For children, make healthy, fun snacks. (Ants on a log: Celery sticks cut longways, spread peanut butter over the surface and stick raisins on top)

Remember:

- Set a good example for children with healthy snacks for yourself.
- Cut out soda and other pre-sweetened drinks.
- Drink water or milk.
- Remember, it's just a snack (if real hunger is being experienced, eat a real meal).
- Choose whole-grain snack or crackers.
- Don't eat snacks while engaged in another activity, like TV watching.
- Eat mindfully.
- Think ahead and be prepared by packing snacks for on the go.

Mindful Eating – The key is "intentional choices"

- Pay attention to stomach signals indicating it is full, then stop eating.
- Learn the difference between true hunger and emotional eating.
- Randomly opening cabinets and checking the fridge usually means boredom, not hunger.
- Be aware of emotions. During emotionally stressful times, it is easy to reach for unhealthy comfort foods.

- Intentionally choose nutritious food.
- Avoid multitasking and eating.
- Avoid watching TV or being on your phone while eating.
- Eat slowly. It takes about 20 minutes for your brain to get the message "I am full." Eating quickly means overeating.
- Plan meals in advance.
- Become familiar with and monitor serving sizes.

Holiday Tips – Holding steady is success

- Make fruit, vegetables, beans, and fish a priority; they are often forgotten.
- Start each meal by eating the vegetables.
- Do not skip meals to "save" calories for the big dinner.
- If you plan on drinking, alternate it with water.
- Ideally, cut out alcohol.
- Don't drink on an empty stomach.
- Go for a family walk.
- Limit dessert portions and savor each bite.
- Wait 10-15 minutes to digest before going for seconds.
- At parties, start with a small plate and add all food groups.
- Eat a healthy snack before going out with friends.
- When socializing, don't stand right next to the food table.
- Stay hydrated.

- Start new traditions that are not centered on food. Instead, engage in family activities. For example, if you make advent calendars, don't fill them with candy; instead, make an "Acts of Kindness Advent Calendar." Or draw, recite or share a favorite holiday memory, etc.

Budgeting – Eating healthy on a budget is possible

- Stop eating out.
- Determine how much is spent on food per week and what you would like to spend per week in the future, then follow it.
- Eat all leftovers in a timely fashion. Clean out your fridge.
- Only buy items on the grocery list.

- Cut out non-essentials like alcohol, cigarettes, and desserts.
- Compare prices at different grocery stores.
- Buy fruits and vegetables that are in season.
- If you live in a state or area where you must pay for bags, remember to bring your own.
- Don't shop when you are hungry.
- Grow food items at home.
- Try meatless Mondays weekly.
- Buy only items you will eat.
- Do not buy something just because it is on sale. Stick to the list.

Spices

Foods have their own flavor. In addition to the flavor of individual foods, flavor comes from four other sources: fat, sugar, salt, and spices. The first three are often consumed in excess. Consuming these in excess has been linked to health concerns. On the other hand, spices have been associated with health benefits. It is recommended that dieters discover and use various spices for flavor over fat, sugar, and salt.

Herbs & Spices	Complements
Basil	Chives, dill, garlic, ginger, lemongrass, mint, parsley, cilantro, bay leaf, coriander, garlic, oregano, mint, parsley, marjoram, rosemary, thyme, salt, pepper, lemon
Curry	Cinnamon, coriander, fennel, ginger, nutmeg, clove, cardamom, cumin, tamarind, turmeric
Cocoa/dark choc.	Lemon, chili powder, lavender, paprika, black peppercorn, wasabi, saffron, pink peppercorn, ginger, ylang ylang, sesame, milk, chipotle, jalapeno, cinnamon, cream cheese
Cinnamon	Anise, cloves, cardamom, coriander, turmeric, ginger, nutmeg, cumin, fennel, garlic, sweet basil, star anise, honey, brown sugar, chocolate, apple, pork, lemongrass
Cilantro	Basil, chives, garlic, oregano, mint, parsley, rosemary, thyme, turmeric, coriander, coconut milk, curry leaf, fennel, ginger, lemongrass, cinnamon, mint, scallions, tarragon
Dill	Basil, garlic, parsley, cumin, ginger, turmeric, onion, yogurt, celery, pumpkin, thyme, mint, oregano, paprika, fennel, peppers
Flax Seed	Fennel seed, paprika
Garlic	Coriander, parsley, thyme, caraway, cilantro, lemongrass, ginger, mint, basil, chives, fennel, cumin, nutmeg, cloves, cardamom, curry leaves, paprika, oregano, dill, turmeric, marjoram, five spice, scallions, onion, rosemary
Ginger	Basil, cilantro, coconut, garlic, lime, lemongrass, mint, scallions, turmeric, mushroom, beet root, fruits, grapes
Honey	Lavender, rosemary, sage, thyme, mint, lemon, lemon balm, vanilla, cinnamon, star anise, chamomile, lime, ginger, garlic, nuts, butter, cheese, salt, black pepper, fruit, tea
Mustard	Bay, coriander, cumin, dill, fennel, garlic, parsley, tarragon, turmeric, honey, apricot, pear, basil
Oregano	Garlic, parsley, sage, chives, pepper, basil, onion, cilantro, marjoram, mint, savory
Parsley	Bay leaf, thyme, tarragon, oregano, garlic, mint
Rosemary	Bay, chives, garlic, lavender, mint, oregano, parsley, sage, thyme
Saffron	Cinnamon, cumin, cilantro, rosemary, thyme, paprika, turmeric, garlic, citrus
Tarragon	Chives, parsley, chervil, coriander, thyme, anise, mustard seed, cress, dill, mint, sorrel, savory, basil
Thyme	Basil, garlic, lavender, nutmeg, oregano, parsley, rosemary
Turmeric	Cilantro, cloves, coconut, coriander, cumin, curry leaf, fennel, garlic, ginger, lemon grass
Vanilla	Allspice, cinnamon, cardamom, ginger, cloves, citrus, rum

Especially for College Students – Establish Healthy Habits Now

College students are in a unique situation. Choices made and habits developed during these years can determine the trajectory of health. Most colleges and university dining halls have abundant variety, which can be both good and bad. Making wise choices when eating in the dining hall is a necessity. For students wishing to eat in their dorm rooms, below are some suggestions.

Experiencing Dorm Life

While living in a dorm, get the following:

- Food storage containers
- Microwave
- Hotplate
- Blender
- Toaster oven
- Mini-fridge
- Knife set
- Can opener
- A few pots and pans

Good food items to keep available in the dorm include:

- Peanut Butter
- Hummus
- Fresh and dried fruits
- Applesauce cups
- Whole wheat tortillas
- Salsa
- Granola or other cold cereal
- Energy bars
- String Cheese
- Graham crackers
- Yogurt
- Pre-washed or pre-cut fresh vegetables
- Nuts
- Oatmeal
- Bagels
- Eggs
- Canned tuna and chicken (packaged in water)
- Trail mix
- Popcorn
- Rice cakes
- Canned beans

When first getting started, buy only the basics.

Don't keep too many snacks around.

Do not stock up on too many non-perishable food items.

Track food intake with an app like My Fitness Pal or Cronometer.

Plan ahead by creating single-serving portions of snacks.

Schedule/Time

Take time to plan ahead.

Make a schedule and stick with it.

Establish a breakfast routine.

Schedule exercise.

Take a nutrition class.

Find an accountability partner.

Schedule time for social media.

Keep a refillable water bottle with you.

Habits

Now is the time to start new habits. Habits become harder to break the longer you do them.

Introduce one new habit at a time.

Work on one habit at a time until it becomes natural and a part of your life.

Commit to a specific habit for 30 days.

Anchor the new habit to something you already do regularly, preferably daily.

Be sure to carve out time every day to consistently do it.

Make a habit stick by turning it into an automatic behavior.

Be content with baby steps.

Make tiny commitments and focus on small wins; just be consistent!

Make a plan ahead of time for when obstacles emerge.

Reward milestones accomplished.

Track your progress.

References

10 Tips for Healthy Snacking. United Dairy Industry of Michigan. https://www.milkmeansmore.org/10-tips-healthy-snacking/. Published June 28, 2018. Accessed June 15, 2020.

A Nutritionist's Tips for Eating Healthy While Traveling. Food Network. https://www.foodnetwork.com/healthyeats/healthy-tips/2016/11/a-nutritionists-tips-for-eating-healthy-while-traveling. Accessed June 15, 2020.

Department of Health & Human Services. 10 Tips for Healthy Shopping. Better Health Channel. https://www.betterhealth.vic.gov.au/health/ten-tips/10-tips-for-healthy-shopping. Published September 30, 2012. Accessed June 15, 2020.

Fogg BJ. *Tiny Habits: The Small Changes That Change Everything.* London: Virgin Books; 2011.

Harvard Health Publishing. 7 Ways to Snack Smarter. Harvard Health. https://www.health.harvard.edu/staying-healthy/7-ways-to-snack-smarter. Accessed June 15, 2020.

Jones J. 11 Holiday Healthy-Eating Tips From A Registered Dietitian. *SELF.* https://www.self.com/story/13-holiday-healthy-eating-tips-from-a-registered-dietitian. Published August 27, 2018. Accessed June 15, 2020.

Laura. 10 Food Budgeting Tips I Wish I Followed Religiously. Mother Would Know. https://motherwouldknow.com/10-food-budgeting-tips-i-wish-i-followed-religiously-html/. Published March 16, 2018. Accessed June 15, 2020.

Ramsey Solutions. How to Save Money on Groceries. daveramsey.com. https://www.daveramsey.com/blog/ways-to-save-on-groceries. Published April 24, 2020. Accessed June 15, 2020.

Rhodes T. *Your Cheat Sheet to Healthy Dorm Room Snacking.* UPMC Pinnacle. https://www.pinnaclehealth.org/wellness-library/blog-and-healthwise/blog-home/post/your-cheat-sheet-to-healthy-dorm-room-snacking. Published 2019. Accessed June 15, 2020.

Schupak A. 12 Mindful Eating Tips That Will Change Your Relationship With Food. *SELF.* https://www.self.com/story/mindfulness-healthy-eating-weight-loss. Published May 25, 2017. Accessed June 15, 2020.

Skerrett PJ. 12 Tips for Holiday Eating. Harvard Health Blog. https://www.health.harvard.edu/blog/12-tips-for-holiday-eating-201212245718. Published August 29, 2019. Accessed June 15, 2020.

Staff FE. Tips for Eating Healthy During the Holidays. familydoctor.org. https://familydoctor.org/tips-eating-healthy-holidays/. Published March 25, 2020. Accessed June 15, 2020.

The Editors of Easy Home Cooking Magazine. Quick Tips for Fast Meals. HowStuffWorks. https://recipes.howstuffworks.com/tools-and-techniques/quick-tips-for-fast-meals.htm. Published November 13, 2007. Accessed June 15, 2020.

Tips For Eating Out - National Heart, Lung, and Blood ... NIH. https://www.nhlbi.nih.gov/health/educational/healthdisp/pdf/tipsheets/Tips-for-Eating-Out.pdf. Accessed June 15, 2020.

Today Show. 7 Tips to Make Weeknight Meals Fast, Easy and Cheap. TODAY.com. https://www.today.com/health/7-tips-make-weeknight-meals-faster-easier-t113992. Published July 19, 2017. Accessed June 15, 2020.

Willard C, Markle E, Kuyken W, et al. 6 Ways to Practice Mindful Eating. *Mindful.* https://www.mindful.org/6-ways-practice-mindful-eating/. Published November 19, 2019. Accessed June 15, 2020.

Writers S. Dining in the Dorm Room: Healthy Food Options & Recipes. AffordableCollegesOnline.org. https://www.affordablecollegesonline.org/college-resource-center/dorm-room-recipes/. Published June 15, 2020. Accessed June 15, 2020.

Writers S. How to Eat Healthy & Stay in Shape While Traveling for Work. LearnHowToBecome.org. https://www.learnhowtobecome.org/career-resource-center/healthy-business-travel/. Published April 21, 2019. Accessed June 15, 2020.

Zelman KM. 10 Tips for Healthy Grocery Shopping. WebMD. https://www.webmd.com/food-recipes/features/10-tips-for-healthy-grocery-shopping. Accessed June 15, 2020.

Made in the USA
Monee, IL
16 January 2024